CONTENTS

Grade 4

UNIT 1: REFLECTIONS

McGraw-Hill School Division

UNIT 3: OUR VOICES

UNIT 4: JUST CURIOUS

UNIT 5: MAKE A PLAN

McGraw-Hill School Division

UNIT 6: SORTING IT OUT

McGraw-Hill School Division

Story Elements

Stories tell about **characters**. Characters can be people or animals. The **setting** is where and when a story takes place.

Read each story. Write the name of the main or most important character and tell what the setting is.

Tamika was upset. Her soccer team had just lost the big game. Now her victory camping trip to the lake would not happen. She stood on the soccer field shaking her head. Her coach smiled and said there would be other games to win.

1. **Main Character** _____

2. **Setting** _____

Our scout leader is great. At our scout meeting last night I think I may have made her unhappy. She asked us to name our favorite scout activities. I said I enjoyed the project we did cleaning up the empty lot. But I hated the fishing trip. Then she said she liked the fishing trip most.

3. **Main Character** _____

4. **Setting** _____

You should see Willie's dog, Byron. This dog does all sorts of funny things. When Willie shines a flashlight, Byron chases the light all over the house. Byron likes to walk around with a towel in his mouth. Then he shakes his head throwing the towel over his face.

5. **Main Character** _____

6. **Setting** _____

At Home: Have students choose a setting in which to place themselves as the main character. Then have them tell a story with themselves in it.

Vocabulary

Read each clue. Then find the vocabulary word in the row of letters and circle it.

brand new	compass	darted	mug	muttered	talker

1. never used   d e b r a n d n e w t s z

2. use it to find direction   b e c o m p a s s r n y

3. moved fast   r e t d a r t e d n g l y

4. big cup with handle   c a l m u g r e j d m l

5. spoke unclearly   w e m u t t e r e d l a r g a

6. one who talks   m a c t a l k e r a y d

6

Reteach 3

Story Comprehension

Write a ✔ next to every sentence that tells about "The Lost Lake."

_____ **1.** Luke and Dad went on a camping trip.

_____ **2.** Dad often talked to Luke for hours at home.

_____ **3.** Dad liked to be with lots of other people at the lake.

_____ **4.** Dad and Luke went looking for their own lake.

_____ **5.** Dad was like a mountain goat on the trail.

_____ **6.** Dad and Luke had to look out for bears.

_____ **7.** Luke never tired while hiking in the woods.

_____ **8.** Dad and Luke got to know each other better on their trip.

At Home: Have students retell the story of "The Lost Lake" in their own words.

2–3

Book 4/Unit 1
The Lost Lake

8

Use Parts of a Book

> Knowing the different **parts of a book** and how to use them can save time and provide important information.

On the lines below, write the letter that matches each book part with its description.

_____ **1.** Table of Contents   **a.** defines important words in a book

_____ **2.** Index   **b.** list of topics and important names in alphabetical order

_____ **3.** Glossary   **c.** list of chapters, unit titles, or selections

Circle the letter of the correct response.

4. In what part of a book would you look to find a word's pronunciation?

    a. index

    b. glossary

    c. table of contents

5. To find on which page a chapter begins, you would look at the

    a. index

    b. glossary

    c. table of contents

6. To find the page on which a topic is discussed, you would look at the

    a. index

    b. title page

    c. table of contents

6   Book 4/Unit 1
The Lost Lake

At Home: Have students write a table of contents for a book they would like to read, or perhaps write.

4

Story Elements

> Knowing who the **characters** in a story are and what the **setting** is helps you better understand and enjoy the story.

Read each story. Circle the letter beside the correct response.

Jessica and her Mom were on their way to her Grandma's house at the lake. Jessica looked at Mom as she drove. Her Mom looked worried. Jessica looked at the road, then back at Mom. She realized that because grandma was ill, Mom now had to take care of Grandma as well as her own family.

1. Who are the main characters?

   a. Jessica and Mom   **b.** Grandma and Mom   **c.** Mom's family

Juan liked spending time with Freddie and his friends at the park. Freddie was fun to be with, but Juan didn't like it when the others started teasing the new boy, Hank. When Juan saw Hank about to run off, Juan walked over to him and asked him to come to his house.

2. What is the setting?

   a. Juan's house   **b.** neighborhood park   **c.** school yard

Dad and Dan usually went to the lake to fish, but not this time. Today they were at the ocean to catch some big, big fish. Neither said a word as each kept his eyes on the sparkling waves. The other fishers along the shore were silent and still, too, as they fished.

3. Who are the main characters?

   a. the other fishermen   **b.** Dad and Dan   **c.** the fish

4. What is the setting?

   a. the ocean   **b.** a lake   **c.** a boat

At Home: Have students choose a familiar story and change its setting to see how such a change affects the events of the story.

McGraw-Hill School Division

Make Inferences

Authors do not always directly state what is happening or how characters are feeling in a story. Sometimes you have to use clues in the story and what you know from your own experiences to help you **make inferences**.

Read the story. Then write complete sentences to answer the questions.

Lucas sat perfectly still as Ms. Sanchez returned the tests. Lucas had studied very hard. He had even missed a camping trip to spend more time studying. When Ms. Sanchez gave Alex his test, he looked at it, then crumpled it up. Jean took hers and kissed the paper. Lucas reached out and took his test from Ms. Sanchez. He took one quick look. Lucas just sat and grinned.

1. How did Alex do on the test? How do you know?

_____

_____

2. How did Jean do? How do you know?

_____

_____

3. Was Lucas happy with his test results? How do you know?

_____

_____

4. Why do you think the room was so quiet?

_____

_____

At Home: Have students explain how their own experiences in taking tests and finding out their grades helped them make inferences about the story.

Multiple-Meaning Words

> Some words have **multiple meanings**, or more than one meaning. Use the other words in the sentences below as clues to help you decide which meaning is correct.

Circle the letter beside the correct meaning for the underlined word.

1. The camper used a <u>saw</u> to cut the log.

   a. a tool used to cut wood

   b. past tense of *see*

2. They got to the <u>park</u> early.

   a. a recreation area

   b. to leave a car in a place for a time

3. He wondered if he had the <u>right</u> directions.

   a. correct

   b. the opposite of left

4. His knapsack was <u>light</u>.

   a. not heavy

   b. cause to catch fire

5. We could not <u>bear</u> the crowds at the lake.

   a. a large animal

   b. put up with

6. It took just a <u>second</u> to the find the map.

   a. a very short amount of time

   b. next after the first

At Home: Have students choose three of the underlined words to use in sentences that show their other meanings.

Book 4/Unit 1
The Lost Lake

7

6

McGraw-Hill School Division

Problem and Solution

> Like someone in real life, a character in a story may have a **problem**. What the character does to find a **solution** to the problem makes up the **plot**, or main events, of the story.

Read the story. Then answer each question.

Sam felt left out. Willa and Lee were staying after school to build a rocket. Sam wanted to work on the rocket too.

Sam decided to ask Willa and Lee if he could help. They said sure, but that he would have to ask Mr. Ward, the science teacher. Mr. Ward said Sam could help if it was okay with his Mom that he stay after school. Sam called his Mom and she told Mr. Ward it was fine for Sam to stay.

Sam was a big help to Willa and Lee. He figured out how to get the rocket to blast-off. They launched the rocket the next day for the science class. All the kids cheered, and Sam was proud.

1. What was Sam's problem? _____

_____

2. What did Sam do first to try to solve the problem? _____

_____

3. What did Sam do next to help solve his problem? _____

_____

4. What was the last thing Sam did to find a solution? _____

_____

McGraw-Hill School Division

4
Book 4/Unit 1
Amelia's Road

At Home: Have students think of other ways Sam might have solved his problem.

8

30

Vocabulary

Use the words from the list to complete the sentence.

accidental	labored	occasions	rhythms	shortcut	shutters

1. She just happened to find the secret door; it was an _____ discovery.

2. The boys took a _____ across the yard to catch the dog.

3. Birthdays are _____ I like to celebrate.

4. The farmers _____ in the fields all day.

5. Our house has yellow _____ on all the windows.

6. We sat on shore and watched the _____ of the waves.

Reteach 10

Story Comprehension

Write the answers to these questions about "Amelia's Road."

1. Why did Amelia cry whenever her father took out the map? _____

   _____

2. What work did Amelia do each morning before school? _____

   _____

3. How did Mrs. Ramos help Amelia at school? _____

   _____

4. What happened by accident in the story? _____

   _____

At Home: Have students write a paragraph about a place that is special to them.

Book 4/Unit 1
Amelia's Road /4

McGraw-Hill School Division

Use a Glossary

> A **glossary**, which is like a small dictionary at the back of a book, can give you important information about a word you may not know. It tells:
>
> the word's meaning as it is used in the book;
>
> how to say the word correctly;
>
> what part of speech the word is (noun, verb, and so on).

commotion   A noisy confusion; disorder. When the campers disturbed the nesting birds, there was a *commotion*.
  com·mo·tion (kə mō′ shən) *noun, plural* **commotions**

companion   A person who often goes along with another; friend; comrade. We three campers were constant *companions* during the summer.
  com·pan·ion (kəm pan′ yən) *noun, plural* **companions**

compass   An instrument for showing directions. A *compass* has a magnetic needle that points to the north.
  com·pass (kum′ pəs) *noun, plural* **compasses**

Use the part of a glossary shown above to answer the questions.

1. In what kind of order are the glossary words arranged?

   _____

2. What does the word commotion mean?

   _____

3. What is a compass helpful for?

   _____

4. What part of speech are the three glossary words?

   _____

5. What is the plural form of *compass*?

   _____

McGraw-Hill School Division

Book 4/Unit 1
Amelia's Road
5

At Home: Have students make a four-word glossary for a favorite storybook to help younger readers enjoy the same book.

11

Problem and Solution

> Knowing how to identify the **problem** a story character has and paying attention to how he or she goes about finding a **solution** will help you better understand the whole story.

Read the stories. Then write what the problems and the solutions are.

Sven is upset about his homework. He is trying to do a math problem but can't figure it out. He reads the directions over and over, but they don't make sense to him. Finally he gives up and goes to bed.

The next morning, Sven goes to school early so he can talk to his teacher. Mrs. Perry understands why Sven is confused and promises to teach the whole class how to solve the problem.

1. **Problem:** _____

_____

2. **Solution:** _____

_____

Tessa wants to add some new things to her special treasure box. She looks all over the house and can't find it in any of the usual places she keeps it.

Tessa sits down to think about where her box could be and remembers the last time she looked in it. She was at Lucia's house. She calls Lucia. The box is there!

3. **Problem:** _____

_____

4. **Solution:** _____

_____

At Home: Have students make up a problem for a character. Then suggest they work with a friend to find some solutions.

12

Book 4/Unit 1
Amelia's Road | 4

McGraw-Hill School Division

Make Inferences

Sometimes you must read especially carefully to pick up clues about characters and events. When you use clues and what you know from your own life, you are **making inferences**.

The sunny room was filled with rows of plant experiments. There were books all along one wall. Margarita saw books about animals, the planets, electricity, and many other subjects. In the storage corner there were piles of safety goggles and plastic gloves. Margarita wasn't sure whether to go in or not. She just waited by the door.

The teacher waved for Margarita to come inside. He pointed to an empty seat and then introduced himself. Others in the room did the same. Before long, Margarita felt right at home.

Use clues in the story to answer the questions.

1. Where was Margarita? _____

_____

2. What kind of room was she looking into? _____

_____

3. How do you know what kind of room it was? _____

_____

4. How do you think Margarita felt as she stood at the door? _____

_____

5. How do you know Margarita was probably a new student? _____

_____

Book 4/Unit 1
Amelia's Road
5

At Home: Have students make up an oral story, giving clues about the setting but not identifying it directly. Ask them to have someone infer the setting.

13

Synonyms and Antonyms

> **Synonyms** are words that have almost the same meaning.
> **Antonyms** are words that have the opposite meaning.

Read each sentence. Write the word from the list that means almost the same as the underlined word.

stay	happiness	completed	rushed

1. She wants to <u>remain</u> in this town. _____

2. I <u>finished</u> my drawing first. _____

3. I <u>hurried</u> along the path to the lake. _____

4. The <u>joy</u> she showed made us smile. _____

Read each sentence. Write the word from the list that means the opposite of the underlined word.

curved	silent	cried	lways

5. Follow the <u>straight</u> road north for two miles. _____

6. The children were unusually <u>noisy</u>. _____

7. She <u>laughed</u> just thinking of the movie. _____

8. Marco is <u>never</u> late. _____

At Home: Have students list three pairs of synonyms and three pairs of antonyms.

14

Book 4/Unit 1
Amelia's Road 8

McGraw-Hill School Division

Story Elements

Characters = Who the story is about
Setting = Where and when the story takes place
Plot = What happens in the story

Read each story. Then write the answer to each question.

Alex lives on a dairy farm in Vermont. It is summer, and he is helping his Dad. They wake up early to milk the cows. Then they go out to the fields to cut hay. Alex is tired, but he knows they can't stop working. He has to help his Dad get the hay cut before a storm comes in. Finally, late in the afternoon, the hay is cut and they take a break in the cool house.

1. Who are the characters? _____

_____

2. What is the setting? _____

_____

3. What are two things that happen in the story? _____

_____

_____

Louisa lives in an apartment in the city. It is school vacation, but Louisa can't sleep late because the street corner below is already busy and noisy. Louisa hears brakes screech and truck doors slam. She gets up and goes downstairs to have breakfast.

4. Who is the main character? _____

_____

5. What is the setting? _____

_____

6. What are two things that happen in the story? _____

_____

At Home: Have students choose either story and add more events to the plot.

McGraw-Hill School Division

Vocabulary

Read each clue. Then write the correct word from the list.

| huddled | overalls | reins | squall | pesky | eerie |

1. This word is an action word. _____

2. This word names a piece of clothing. _____

3. This word names a kind of storm. _____

4. This word describes annoying behavior. _____

5. This word names something used with horses. _____

6. This word describes something strange and scary. _____

Story Comprehension

Circle the letter beside the answer to each question about "Sarah, Plain and Tall."

1. Why did Sarah leave Maine and come to the prairie?

   a. to have a vacation   **b.** to answer Papa's ad

2. Who told Sarah there will always be things to miss?

   a. Papa   **b.** Maggie

3. How did Papa feel when Sarah helped with the roof?

   a. surprised   **b.** angry

4. What did Sarah want to learn to do?

   a. work in the field   **b.** drive a wagon

At Home: Have students write sentences using three of the vocabulary words.

16–17

Book 4/Unit 1
Sarah, Plain and Tall   4

Use a Table of Contents and Headings

> The **table of contents** gives you an idea of what the chapters in a book are about. It also gives page numbers. **Headings** in a section of text also give you an idea of what you will read about.

Table of Contents

Chapter 2   *Work Horses*

On the Farm

This breed of horses is the strongest and heaviest of all other horse breeds. Years ago these horses did the work that heavy farm machinery does today. They pulled wagons great distances and hauled plows through the fields.

Coach Horses

Another type of work horse is called the Heavy Harness Horse, or the Coach Horse. These horses are good for light farm work, pleasure riding, or pulling coaches or buggies.

Use the samples to answer these questions.

1. What is the whole book about? _____

   _____

2. What is the title of Chapter 4? _____

3. To learn about ponies, which chapter would you read? _____

4. What is the first heading in Chapter 2? _____

5. What page would you check to read about race horses? _____

At Home: Have students find the Table of Contents in a book and explain how it helps readers.

Story Elements

As they read good readers keep track of the most important story elements: **characters**, **setting**, and the events that make up the **plot**.

Read the story. Then fill in the story map that follows.

Jackie spent most of the day at the department store. Her mom had suggested that she look for holiday gifts that didn't cost too much. Jackie wanted to find just the right gift for each of her three friends. And she did. She found a glass horse for Jennifer, a cloth purse for Ariel, and a book about lighthouses in Maine for René.

When Jackie returned home that evening, she and her mom went to work with lots of boxes and wrapping. They made each package as special as the gift inside. After dinner, Jackie was ready to deliver her gifts.

1. Characters	_____
2. Setting # 1	_____
3. Setting # 2	_____
4. Event	_____
5. Event	_____
6. Event	_____
7. Event	_____
8. Ending	_____

At Home: Have students make a similar story map for a story they especially like.

Book 4/Unit 1
Sarah, Plain and Tall

19

8

McGraw-Hill School Division

Problem and Solution

> Sometimes one character's **problem** can affect other characters in the story. Often the other characters help find a **solution** to the problem.

Read the story. Then fill in the chart that follows.

Kelly wanted to get a pet. All her friends had pets.

Kelly had asked for a puppy for the past two birthdays, but she didn't get one. Her parents always seemed to avoid the issue. Kelly decided to explain to them how she felt.

Her mom and dad said there would be no one at home to walk the dog during the day. Dad asked, "What about a cat?"

But Kelly and her mom were worried that a cat would be too lonely by itself all day. "What about two kittens?" asked Dad. "They could keep each other company." Kelly liked the idea!

Kelly's Problem	**Kelly's Solution**
She wants a pet of her own.	1.
Mom and Dad's Problem 2.	**Dad's Solution** 3.
Mom and Kelly's Problem 4.	**Dad's Solution** 5.

At Home: Have students extend the story, adding new problems caused by the kittens and some possible solutions.

Synonyms and Antonyms

> **Synonyms** are words that have almost the same meaning.
> **Antonyms** are words that have the opposite meaning.

Read each sentence. Write the word from the list that means almost the same as the underlined word.

closed	glad	huge	smiled

1. After everyone was inside, we shut the door and _____ the windows.

2. Large clouds covered the sky and _____ drops of rain fell.

3. We were happy to be safe, and Papa was _____, too.

4. I grinned and Papa _____ back.

Read each sentence. Write the word from the list that means the opposite of the underlined word.

softly	followed	dark	outside

5. The children talked loudly, but she spoke _____.

6. The light faded and we were left in the _____.

7. Inside it was calm, but _____ it was stormy.

8. Papa led the way to the house, and we _____.

At Home: Have students think of two pairs of synonyms and two pairs of antonyms to write in sentences.

21

Book 4/Unit 1
Sarah, Plain and Tall

8

McGraw-Hill School Division

Main Idea and Supporting Details

> To find the **main idea**, ask yourself what the text you are reading is mostly about. Look for **supporting details** that tell more about the main idea.

Read the following and circle the letter beside the correct responses.

Recycling products is good for the environment. When we reuse paper, plastic and metal, fewer natural resources have to be used. Recycling also reduces garbage. It shows that people care about using our resources wisely. Almost everywhere in our country, communities are passing laws to make people recycle.

1. Which is the main idea?

   a. People should not waste plastic.

   b. Recycling is good for the environment.

2. Which is a supporting detail?

   a. Recycling reduces garbage.

   b. There are not enough natural resources.

3. Which is <u>not</u> a detail that tells more about the main idea?

   a. Almost everywhere communities are passing laws to make people recycle.

   b. Recycling helps people use resources wisely.

4. Which is <u>not</u> a fact according to the text?

   a. Recycling means fewer natural resources have to be used up.

   b. All people care about using our resources wisely.

Book 4/Unit 1
Seal Journey
4

At Home: Have students read a section of one of their textbooks and list the main idea and at least two supporting details.

22

Vocabulary

Read each clue. Then find the vocabulary word in the row of letters and circle it.

assured	horizon	jagged	mature	nursery	squealed

1. grown up   b e t u m a t u r e p l s w

2. earth and sky boundary   l h o r i z o n j g f d a z c

3. told in a positive way   k a w j w a s s u r e d b c

4. an area for babies or young h a y n u r s e r y l t e r

5. a high, shrill cry   r e w a r s q u e a l e d t

6. with sharp, uneven edges   m u w a j a g g e d l a c q

Story Comprehension

Circle the letter beside the answer to each question about "Seal Journey."

1. What is the topic of this selection?
   a. harp seals   **b.** polar bears

2. Which describes the setting?
   a. cold and icy   **b.** warm and rainy

3. What do mothers and their pups do to recognize each other?
   a. They lick each other.   **b.** They rub noses.

4. What special thing did Jonah get to do before going home?
   a. He held a pup.   **b.** He fed a pup.

5. Why were the pups killed in the past?
   a. Hunters wanted their white fur.
   b. The animals were disturbing people.

Use an Index

> The **index** at the back of a book is useful if you need to know quickly on which page or pages you can find information.

Airplanes, 42–46
Bicycles, 23–26, 28
Buses, 12, 16, 21–25
Cars, 3–7, 21–25, 52
Railroads, 34–37
Ocean ships, 62–67
Trucks, 12–15, 21–23, 30–32
Transportation, see also specific types
   City transportation, 21–26
   Future of, 47–53
   History of, 30–39

Use the part of an index shown above to answer the questions.

1. On which pages can you find information about ocean ships?

_____

2. On which pages can you find information about trucks?

_____

3. Where would you look to find information about early types of transportation?

_____

4. Where would you look to find out about transportation in 2050?

_____

5. Where can you find information about trains?

_____

6. Does information on trucks come before or after information about airplanes in

the book? _____

Book 4/Unit 1
Seal Journey
6

At Home: Have students find five topics and the corresponding page numbers in a book at home.

25

McGraw-Hill School Division

Main Idea and Supporting Details

> Sometimes authors state the **main idea** and then give **details** to support it. Other times it is up to the reader to decide what the main idea is.

Read the paragraph. Then write the answers to the questions.

> Americans have always loved sports. But the popularity of certain sports has changed over time. Baseball and football used to be the most popular sports in our country. Many people still play and enjoy these games. Today, however, millions of young people are playing soccer. Some schools have dropped football and replaced it with soccer. Gymnastics has also grown in popularity as have volleyball, ice and field hockey, and figure skating.

1. What is the main idea? _____

_____

_____

2. What is one detail that supports the main idea? _____

_____

_____

3. What is another supporting detail? _____

_____

Read the statement that follows. Then answer the question.

> Americans no longer care much about sports.

4. Is the statement true or false based on the paragraph above?

_____

_____

At Home: Have students write a short paragraph about sports with a main idea and two supporting details.

Book 4/Unit 1
Seal Journey
4

26

McGraw-Hill School Division

Make Inferences

> Good readers look for clues in the text that will help them understand what is happening and how characters are feeling. This is called **making inferences**.

Read the story. Then make inferences to answer the questions.

> Brian turned around and around. Everywhere he looked there was only sand. It seemed there were miles of nothing but sand. Brian checked to see if he still had his hat on because he felt like he was getting sunburned. His shirt felt glued to his body. He stretched and could feel every bone in his body. It had been a long ride on the camel. Even though he felt uncomfortable, he knew he would never forget what he was seeing. After one last look, he waved goodbye to the great pyramids.

Write the answer to each question.

1. Where is Brian? What clues let you know? _____

_____

2. Is it hot or cold? How do you know? _____

_____

3. How does Brian's body feel? How do you know? _____

_____

4. Why does he feel this way? _____

_____

5. How does Brian feel as he looks around? _____

_____

_____

McGraw-Hill School Division

5 | Book 4/Unit 1
Seal Journey

At Home: Have students write about inferences they had to make to figure out the plot of a favorite book or movie.

27

Multiple-Meaning Words

> Some words have more than one meaning. These words are called **homographs** if they are always spelled exactly the same way. Even though homographs are spelled the same, some are pronounced differently. An example is: Don't tear the paper. I have a tear in my eye.

Circle the letter beside the meaning of the underlined homograph.

1. The <u>seal</u> pups grow up quickly.

   a. to close something tightly

   b. a mammal that lives in the sea

2. The pup rested at the <u>base</u> of an ice mound.

   a. a military area

   b. the bottom part

3. Seal pups nurse for a short <u>period</u> of time.

   a. certain amount of time

   b. a mark of punctuation

4. The scientists will take a <u>break</u> before traveling on.

   a. to cause to separate into pieces

   b. a rest period

5. Our nature <u>club</u> is planning to go to a nature preserve.

   a. a group of people who join together

   b. a stick used as a weapon

6. The weight of the ice made the tree branches <u>bow</u>.

   a. bend over

   b. a knot of ribbon with two loops

At Home: Ask students to choose three homographs and use them in sentences that show their other meanings.

Book 4/Unit 1
Seal Journey 6

28

McGraw-Hill School Division

Problem and Solution

Often the plot, or what happens in a story, is a matter of the characters finding a **solution** to a **problem**. Sometimes there may even be more than just one problem.

Read the story. Then write to tell the problems and the solution.

Shandra and LuAnn volunteered to come up with ideas to help their soccer team. The team needed a field for practice and money to buy new uniforms.

On the way to LuAnn's house, Shandra passed an empty lot. "What a mess!" she thought. It was full of empty bottles and cans. When she got to LuAnn's house the girls talked about their soccer team assignment. They thought and thought, but neither had any ideas. All of a sudden, Shandra stood up. "I've got the answer!" she said. "Do you know that empty lot nearby? We can clear it for a practice field. The owner of the lot is a friend of my parents. I know he'll let us use it for practice. We can return the cans and bottles we collect to the store and use the money we get for uniforms."

1. Problem 1: _____

2. Problem 2: _____

3. Solution to both problems: _____

_____

_____

4. What might be a problem with the girls' solution? _____

_____

_____

Book 4/Unit 1
Open Wide, Don't Bite!
4

At Home: Have students try to think of other solutions to the girls' problem.

29

Vocabulary

Write a word from the list to complete each sentence.

broad	fangs	patients	healthy	reptiles	skills

1. Doctors treat _____ with different problems.

2. Do you think a crocodile has a _____ smile?

3. The goal of a doctor is to keep people _____.

4. Big cats have _____ that help them grab and tear meat.

5. Medical schools teach doctors the _____ they need.

6. Crocodiles and lizards are _____.

Story Comprehension

Write complete sentences to answer the following questions about "Open Wide, Don't Bite!"

1. What kind of doctor is Dr. Kertesz?

_____

2. What does Dr. Kertesz do on Fridays?

_____

3. How does Dr. Kertesz keep animals from getting upset?

_____

4. What size animal is easiest for Dr. Kertesz to work on?

_____

5. How does Dr. Kertesz's work help animals?

_____

At Home: Have students make a list of unusual occupations they know about.

Book 4/Unit 1
Open Wide, Don't Bite! 5

30–31

McGraw-Hill School Division

Use Headings, Captions, and Sidebars

Headings, captions, and sidebars all make it easier to read information. **Headings** help you find specific information. **Captions** and **sidebars** give you additional facts.

Look at this page from a book about veterinarians. Then answer the questions.

A Veterinarian's Tools

A vet uses the same types of tools as a doctor who takes care of people. Two of these tools are the stethoscope and the thermometer.

A vet uses a stethoscope to listen to an animal's heartbeat.

There are many different kinds of veterinarians. Some vets care for pets. Others work with farm animals. Still others take care of zoo animals.

1. What is the heading on this page?

_____

2. What additional information does the sidebar give you?

_____

3. How many captions are on this page?

_____

4. How do headings, captions, and sidebars help you read?

_____

McGraw-Hill School Division

Book 4/Unit 1
Open Wide, Don't Bite!
4

At Home: Have students identify headings, captions, and sidebars in their science or social studies texts.

32

Main Idea and Supporting Details

The **main idea** of a selection or a part of the text is the most important idea the author wants to get across. **Supporting details** give more information about the main idea.

Read the text and fill in the chart.

The African elephant is the largest land animal. Everything about it is big. It weighs more than 16,000 pounds and is 20 feet long. This elephant weighs about as much as about 17 pick-up trucks or 200 fourth graders weighing 80 pounds each. In addition to a huge body, the African elephant has a huge nose, or trunk. A trunk is so big and so strong that it can lift and carry a load weighing 2,000 pounds. Its tusks are long, curved teeth but they are not used for eating. The elephants also have back teeth called molars that can be as big as one foot long.

1. **Main Idea:** _____

2. **Supporting Detail:** _____

3. **Supporting Detail:** _____

4. **Supporting Detail:** _____

5. Is the statement below true or false based on what you read?

   Trunks are long teeth that are not very strong. _____

6. Rewrite the statement above to make it correct. _____

   _____

At Home: Have students write more details to support the main idea of the paragraph.

33

Book 4/Unit 1
Open Wide, Don't Bite! 6

McGraw-Hill School Division

Multiple-Meaning Words

Some words are spelled the same, but have **multiple meanings**. These words are called **homographs**. Use the clues before and after the underlined word in each sentence to figure out the correct meaning of the homograph.

Circle the letter beside the correct meaning for the underlined word.

1. The doctor keeps spare blankets in an oak <u>chest</u>.

    a. the front of the upper human body

    b. a box or piece of furniture

2. Can the doctor really operate on a <u>bug</u>?

    a. an insect

    b. a mistake in a computer program

3. Hold the kitten tightly so it doesn't <u>fall</u>.

    a. a season of the year

    b. to tumble to the ground

4. The <u>tip</u> of the needle was very sharp.

    a. money you leave for good service

    b. the point or end of an object

5. The dog must <u>fast</u> before the operation.

    a. to not eat

    b. quick

6. If your pets <u>tire</u> easily, they may be sick.

    a. get sleepy

    b. a rubber hoop around a wheel

At Home: Ask students to think of three or four other words that have more than just one meaning.

Synonyms and Antonyms

> **Synonyms** are words that have almost the same meaning.
> **Antonyms** are words that have the opposite meaning.

Draw a line from the sentence to the word that is the synonym for the underlined word in each sentence.

1. Ernesto was sure he had the <u>right</u> answer.   begin

2. Vin found <u>a rare</u> flower in the woods.   illness

3. The doctor had treated this <u>disease</u> before.   still

4. With no wind, the lake appeared perfectly <u>calm</u>.   hard

5. The race will <u>start</u> in one hour.   an uncommon

6. The coach put the team through a <u>difficult</u> practice.   correct

Draw a line from the sentence to the word that is the antonym for the underlined word in each sentence.

7. Frankie had a <u>short</u> vacation.   bad

8. The team played a <u>good</u> game.   long

9. Did you <u>find</u> your book?   sick

10. In winter, the frozen ground is <u>hard</u>.   lose

11. I got the first question <u>wrong</u>.   soft

12. <u>Healthy</u> animals eat well.   right

At Home: Have students read a magazine article and circle words for which they can substitute synonyms or antonyms.

35

Book 4/Unit 1
Open Wide, Don't Bite!   12

McGraw-Hill School Division

Unit 1 Vocabulary Review

A. Write words from the list to complete each sentence.

squall	eerie	reins	mug	broad	shortcut

1. The dark house with its broken windows looked _____

2. The violent _____ caused damage to trees on our street.

3. Dad gets lost when he tries to take a _____.

4. To ride a horse well, you need to know how to handle the

   _____.

5. After sledding I had a _____ of hot chocolate.

6. Plant-eating animals have _____ teeth.

B. Write words from the list to complete the paragraph.

darted	compass	muttered	talker

Terry _____ to herself. She wasn't much of a

_____ and didn't want to ask for help. Was she

lost? She looked at her _____. Then, without a

word she _____ across the field back to the

hikers' path.

At Home: Have students try to use three of the vocabulary words on this page in a single sentence.

Unit 1 Vocabulary Review

A. Read each question. Choose a word from the list to answer the question. Write your answer on the line.

assured	fangs	nursery	patients	horizon

1. If you are on a boat and you see where the sky and sea meet, what are you seeing? _____

2. If you see a tiger without its long front teeth, what is it missing?

_____

3. Where do newborn babies sleep in the hospital? _____

4. If someone told you positively that you were right, what would you feel?

_____

5. When people visit a doctor for treatment, what are they called?

_____

B. Read each clue. Then find the vocabulary word in the row of letters and circle it.

shutters	overalls	labored	huddled	pesky

1. worked very hard   m a q l a b o r e d s e c v

2. crowded together   j h u d d l e d n e r s c

3. work clothes   t h u e s r o v e r a l l s

4. window covers   b a w c s h u t t e r s p a z

5. synonym for *annoying* n o t m d p e s k y l a r j

At Home: Have students look for vocabulary in newspapers and magazines they read and keep a list of the sentences the words are used in.

37

Book 4/Unit 1
Unit 1 Vocabulary Review
10

McGraw-Hill School Division

Make Predictions

When you think ahead about what may or may not happen next in a story, you **make a prediction**.

Read the sentences. Then circle what you think will happen.

1. Annette gives the cashier a $10 bill for a movie ticket that costs $8.50. What do you think Annette will do next?

   a. look for a place to sit

   b. wait for change from the cashier

   c. buy candy

2. Roger loves to be outdoors and to exercise. Today, he is going to the movies. The theater is 1 mile away from home. How do you think he will get there?

   a. walk   **b.** take a bus   **c.** ask his mother for a ride

3. Traci wants to buy a special CD as a gift for a friend. It costs $16 but she has only $10. What do you think Traci might do?

   a. forget about the whole idea

   b. find a way to earn the money that she needs

   c. buy a cheaper CD

4. Nick just remembered that Mia's birthday party is tomorrow. He knows a store that is open for another hour. What do you think Nick will do?

   a. not go to the party

   b. buy a present after the party

   c. hurry to the store

5. Nadine decided to walk rather than take the bus home from school. When she had walked one block, it began to rain. What do you think Nadine will do?

   a. continue walking home

   b. call a friend for a ride

   c. go back and take the bus

Book 4/Unit 2
Justin and the Best Biscuits in the World
5

At Home: Have students watch a favorite television show. At a commercial break, have them predict what will happen next.

38

Vocabulary

Write a word from the list to complete each sentence.

festival	guilt	inspecting	lingered	pranced	resounded

1. We were _____ the boat to make sure it was safe.

2. Ellen _____ at the table long after she had finished her dinner.

3. Jack felt a sense of _____ because of the unkind things he had said to his brother.

4. The horses _____ restlessly in the corral.

5. The sound of the explosion _____ through the night.

6. There will be many bands and good food at the _____.

Story Comprehension

Write a ✔ next to every sentence that tells about "Justin and the Best Biscuits in the World." For help you may look back at the story.

1. _____ Justin has always liked housework.

2. _____ Justin cleared the table and washed the dishes without being asked.

3. _____ Justin learned to fold his shirts and make his bed.

4. _____ Justin was impressed by his grandfather's cooking.

5. _____ Justin helped his grandfather inspect the fence.

6. _____ Justin was bored by stories about Black cowboys.

7. _____ Justin's grandfather was a cowboy but not a broncobuster.

8. _____ Justin learned that it doesn't matter whether women or men do the work when it needs to be done.

At Home: Have students recall two more details from "Justin and the Best Biscuits in the World."

39–40

Book 4/Unit 2
Justin and the Best Biscuits in the World / 8

McGraw-Hill School Division

Use a Dictionary

A **dictionary** tells you what a word means and how to pronounce it. Each entry also tells you if a word is a noun, a verb, or another part of speech.

Use the sample dictionary entries below to answer the questions.

overalls loose-fitting trousers usually having a piece that covers the chest with suspenders attached. The farmer wore *overalls* while doing his chores. **o•ver•alls** (ō′vər ôlz′) *noun plural*

overrun 1. to swarm or spread over or throughout. The invading army had *overrun* the countryside. **2.** to flow over. The river *overran* its banks. **3.** to run beyond. The player always *overruns* second base. **o•ver•run,** (ō′vər run′) *verb* **o•ver•ran, o•ver • run • ning**

1. What does *overalls* mean? _____

   _____

2. How many syllables does *overalls* have? _____

3. What part of speech is *overalls?* _____

4. How many different definitions does *overrun* have? _____

5. What meaning does *overran* have in the sentence that follows? *Foxes*

   overran the ranch. _____

   _____

6. What part of speech is *overrun?* _____

6 Book 4/Unit 2
Justin and the Best Biscuits in the World

At Home: Have students draw a picture of overalls based on the definition given and then label it.

41

Make Predictions

You can use what you know about story characters to **predict**, or think ahead about, what the characters may do.

Read each story below. Then answer the questions.

The horseback riding teacher was curious about why Sandra Sanchez had missed her last three lessons. He knew that the lessons were very important to Sandra's mother. Mrs. Sanchez wanted Sandra to start entering riding contests soon. One day, the riding teacher saw Mrs. Sanchez on the street.

1. What do you think the riding teacher will do?

_____

_____

2. How do you think Sandra's mother will react?

_____

_____

Noah liked every subject but art. Noah's pictures just never looked the way he wanted them to. But a funny thing happened when Noah started painting. Mr. Vass thought that Noah's paintings were good, and asked if Noah would enter them in a contest! Noah smiled with pride. When Noah came home, Noah's parents could see that he was very happy.

3. Do you think that Noah will enter the contest? Explain why.

_____

_____

4. Do you think that Noah will stop painting when the art class moves on to a different topic? Explain.

_____

_____

At Home: Have students make another prediction based on one of the stories.

42

Book 4/Unit 2
Justin and the Best Biscuits in the World 4

McGraw-Hill School Division

Form Generalizations

A **generalization** is a broad statement. It can be about many people, many animals, or many things.

Read the paragraphs below. Put a ✔ next to each generalization that you can make from the facts in the paragraph.

Braille is a system of reading that is used by blind people. It is named for its inventor, Louis Braille. The idea came to him when he noticed a system of sending coded wartime messages by using raised dots on cardboard. By placing raised dots in different positions, Braille made an alphabet, a system of punctuation, and music, that blind people read by running their fingers over the dots. Braille was not accepted officially right away. Today, however, it is used in all written languages.

1. _____ All people accepted the Braille system right away.

2. _____ Today, Braille is widely used in all written languages.

3. _____There is no system for blind people to read music.

Owning a pet can be a rewarding experience. However you should choose a pet carefully. For example, a large dog might be unhappy in a small apartment. A bird or some fish might be a good choice for someone who wants a pet that does not need to be walked or played with. People who are unwilling or unable to take responsibility for a pet are better off choosing not to have one. A pet is a living being that must be cared for.

4. _____ Owning a pet is a responsibility.

5. _____ There is only one correct pet for each owner.

6. _____ To choose a pet, you need to think about how the pet will fit into your home and your life.

McGraw-Hill School Division

---

6 Book 4/Unit 2
Justin and the Best Biscuits in the World

At Home: Have students make a generalization about an article they have read or a television show they have watched.

43

Use Context Clues

Sometimes when you read, you will come to a word that you don't know. You can use **context clues**, or other words or sentences around the unfamiliar word, to help you figure out the meaning of the word.

Circle the letter beside the meaning of the underlined word in each sentence.

1. Grandfather warmed stew and even fried some bread in the skillet.

   a. cooking pan   **b.** type of wagon

2. They see for miles across the treeless, even plains.

   a. hilly green areas   **b.** stretch of flat land

3. Fred searched everywhere, scanning the area for stray cattle.

   a. looking carefully   **b.** ignoring

4. The foreman told the ranch hands what each should do.

   a. boss of a crew   **b.** stranger

5. After tiring, the horse began to canter, and the rider could catch her breath.

   a. run wildly   **b.** move at a slow, steady pace

6. On some ranches, calves are branded to let people know who owns them.

   a. marked with sign   **b.** kept indoors

At Home: Have students tell what context clues they found to help them identify the meanings of skillet and foreman.

44

Book 4/Unit 2
Justin and the Best Biscuits in the World

6

McGraw-Hill School Division

Sequence of Events

> **Sequence** is the order in which things happen. Words such as *before, first,* and *then* can help you understand sequence.

Read the story. Circle the letter beside the answer to each question.

Jed won the marathon by 10 minutes. But it wasn't as easy as it seemed. Before Jed began running, he read about training. Then he started to run short distances. Jed increased the number of miles he ran each week. After 4 months, Jed ran a half-marathon, or 13 miles. Although Jed lost his first race, he trained for another 8 months until he was ready for a full marathon.

1. Which of these events happened first?

   a. Jed won the marathon.

   b. Jed began running.

   c. Jed read all about training.

2. Which of these events happened last?

   a. Jed trained for another 8 months.

   b. Jed won the marathon.

   c. Jed ran a half-marathon.

3. What is the first thing Jed did after he read about training?

   a. Jed increased the number of miles he ran each week.

   b. Jed ran a half-marathon.

   c. Jed started to run short distances.

4. What did Jed do after he lost the half-marathon?

   a. Jed trained for another 8 months.

   b. Jed read about training.

   c. Jed increased the number of miles that he ran each week.

5. How many months of training did Jed need until he won a marathon?

   a. 4   **b.** 8   **c.** 12

McGraw-Hill School Division

5

Book 4/Unit 2
Just a Dream

At Home: Have students describe five things they have done during the day in the order in which the things happened.

45

Vocabulary

Choose the word that matches the meaning. Then fill in the crossword puzzle.

bulging	crumpled	foul	haze	shrieking	waddled

Across

4. crushed; wrinkled

5. mist, smoke, or dust in the air

6. swelling outwards

Down

1. having a bad smell

2. making a shrill noise

3. walked with short steps, swayed from side to side

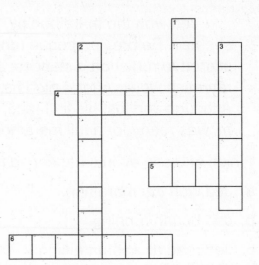

Story Comprehension

Circle the letter beside the words that correctly complete each sentence about "Just a Dream." You may look at the story for help.

1. The wish that started Walter's dream trip was _____.

    a. to live in the future   **b.** to live in the past

2. At the beginning of the story, Walter _____.

    a. cared about litter   **b.** didn't sort garbage

3. When Walter fell asleep, he dreamt about a world that _____.

    a. was dirty and noisy   **b.** was wonderfully clean

4. Walter's dreams made him change how he _____.

    a. cleaned his room   **b.** felt about the environment

At Home: Have students retell "Just a Dream" in their own words.

46–47

Book 4/Unit 2
Just a Dream 4

McGraw-Hill School Division

Use a Thesaurus

> A **thesaurus** is a book that gives synonyms for a word. If you want to add interest to your writing, use a thesaurus.

Use the thesaurus entries to choose the best synonym for the underlined word in each sentence. Circle the correct letter.

> **clean** verb. 1. Volunteers helped *clean* the park.
> *Synonyms:* wash, cleanse, scrub, spruce up, tidy

> **environment** noun. 1. Littering fouls our *environment*.
> *Synonyms:* surroundings, habitat, setting, world, atmosphere

> **trash** noun. 1. Put the *trash* in the can.
> *Synonyms*: waste, garbage, junk, litter
> 2. The expert called the ideas in the report *trash*.
> *Synonyms:* nonsense, foolishness, drivel

1. Norah ignored the article because she thought it was <u>trash</u>.

   a. waste   **b.** litter   **c.** nonsense

2. The government will <u>clean</u> Wild River.

   a. scrub   **b.** cleanse   **c.** litter

3. People know that recycling helps the <u>environment</u>.

   a. world   **b.** setting   **c.** waste

4. The dump was filled with mountains of <u>trash</u>.

   a. nonsense   **b.** garbage   **c.** foolishness

5. We had to use a brush to <u>clean</u> the oil off the floor.

   a. tidy   **b.** scrub   **c.** spruce up

5   Book 4/Unit 2
Just a Dream

At Home: Have students explain why scrub is not the best synonym for clean in the second item.

48

Sequence of Events

Keeping track of **sequence**, or the order in which things happen, can help you better understand and enjoy a story. Look for time clue words to help you identify the sequence.

Read the story and the sentences below. Next to each sentence, write a number from 1 to 8 to show the order in which events happened.

The living room was such a mess! When Mrs. Roper walked in, she couldn't believe that Sam and Janet had cleaned it that afternoon. But they had. Unfortunately, right after they had finished, the first accident happened. Spot jumped up on a table and knocked over the flower pot. That led to the second accident. When Sam tried to vacuum the dirt, the vacuum bag ripped open. Dirt and dust fell all over the floor. Next, Janet slipped on the dirt, and dropped a vase she'd been carrying. A few seconds later, Mrs. Roper walked in.

_____ Janet dropped a vase.

_____ Mrs. Roper walked in.

_____ Sam and Janet cleaned the living room.

_____ The vacuum bag ripped open.

_____ Spot knocked over the flower pot.

_____ Sam tried to vacuum the dirt.

_____ Spot jumped up on a table.

_____ Janet slipped on the dirt.

At Home: Have students think of a few events from "Just a Dream" and list the events in the order in which they happened.

49

Book 4/Unit 2
Just a Dream 8

Form Generalizations

> A **generalization** is a broad statement based on a set of facts.

Read the sentences below. Circle the letter next to the generalization that can be drawn from the facts.

1. Mark plays baseball from April to September. He plays football from October to December. However, Mark likes to play basketball year round.

    a. Mark enjoys many sports.

    b. Mark likes baseball better than football.

    c. Mark wants to be a professional basketball player.

2. After school every day, Paige walks dogs for her neighbors. On some weekends, Paige babysits. Paige also does errands for pay.

    a. Paige spends a lot of money.

    b. Paige does little when she is not in school.

    c. Paige is a hard-working girl.

3. When I told a scary story, Onida yawned. She laughs at horror movies and would skydive, if her mother would let her.

    a. Onida is not easy to scare.

    b. Onida likes movies.

    c. Onida is frightened of many things.

4. Mr. Potter built his own computer. After that, he made an alarm system for his house. He also fixed my broken watch.

    a. Mr. Potter breaks a lot of things.

    b. Mr. Potter spends a lot of time at home.

    c. Mr. Potter is good at making and fixing mechanical things.

5. Manuel writes in his journal every night. He writes stories for his younger brother all the time. He answers letters from his pen pal every week.

    a. Manuel doesn't like sports.

    b. Manuel likes to write.

    c. Manuel does well in math.

McGraw-Hill School Division

Book 4/Unit 2
Just a Dream

At Home: Have students write some facts about themselves and then use the list to make a few generalizations about themselves.

Compound Words

When two words are put together to make one word, the new word is called a **compound word**. You can usually use the meaning of each of the small words to help you figure out the meaning of the compound word.

Look at the compound words below. Write the two smaller words that make up each compound word. Then write the meaning of the compound word.

clothesline

1. Word 1: _____

2. Word 2: _____

3. Meaning: _____

hairbrush

4. Word 1: _____

5. Word 2: _____

6. Meaning: _____

underground

7. Word 1: _____

8. Word 2: _____

9. Meaning: _____

shamefaced

10. Word 1: _____

11. Word 2: _____

12. Meaning: _____

McGraw-Hill School Division

At Home: Ask students to name the small words in the compounds storefront, crosswalk, and foghorn and write the meanings for them.

51

Book 4/Unit 2
Just a Dream
12

Cause and Effect

> A **cause** is the reason something happens. An **effect** is what happens.

Each underlined sentence describes an effect. Circle the letter beside the sentence that tells the cause.

1. After a few minutes, the wind stopped. Terri's sailboat stopped moving. She took out an oar and began to paddle.

   a. Terri began to paddle

   b. Terri took out an oar.

   c. The wind stopped.

2. Noah was overjoyed! The little park was saved from destruction. The volunteers had raised enough money to buy it from developers.

   a. Noah was overjoyed.

   b. Volunteers raised enough money to buy the park.

   c. Developers donated the park to the volunteers.

3. It was only 2:00 in the afternoon, but Sarah turned on her headlights. Clouds had covered the sun, and it was dark.

   a. Clouds blocked the sun.

   b. Some sun came through the clouds.

   c. It was 2:00 in the afternoon.

4. Snow continued for days. Weather forecasters said it was a record snowfall. Schools were shut for three days. Children had fun sledding and playing in the snow.

   a. Children had fun in the snow.

   b. Weather forecasters said it was a record snowfall.

   c. It had snowed.

McGraw-Hill School Division

Book 4/Unit 2
Leah's Pony
4

At Home: Have students describe something that happened during the day and tell why it happened.

Vocabulary

Write a word from the list to complete each sentence.

| bidding | clustered | county | glistened | overflowing | sturdy |

1. Reporters _____ around the baseball star.

2. Meg's eyes _____ with tears.

3. The laundry hamper was _____ with clothes.

4. Mr. Polanski owns the largest farm in the _____.

5. The _____ for the house began at $98,000.

6. Although the table was old and used, it was still _____.

6

Story Comprehension

Write a ✔ next to every sentence that tells something true about "Leah's Pony." You may look back at the story for help.

1. _____ Leah's family were factory workers.

2. _____ Leah's family always had money problems.

3. _____ Some neighbors moved away to find a better place.

4. _____ Leah's family had to sell animals and machines.

5. _____ Leah sold her pony because she was told to.

6. _____ Neighbors helped buy back the family's things.

7. _____ Leah's family was surprised and pleased by her actions.

8. _____ Leah never got back her pony.

At Home: Have students identify their favorite part of "Leah's Pony."

Book 4/Unit 2
Leah's Pony
8

53–54

Choose Reference Sources

> Knowing in which **reference source** to look for information can save you time and provide you with the best answers to your questions.

Use the descriptions that follow to help you answer the questions.

> **Almanac:** Up-to-date information about people, places, and events. The information often appears in a table or chart.
>
> **Atlas:** Many different kinds of maps.
>
> **Dictionary:** Lists words in alphabetical order. A dictionary gives the meaning, pronunciation, and part of speech of a word.
>
> **Encyclopedia:** Articles on many topics, arranged in alphabetical order.
>
> **Thesaurus:** Synonyms or words with almost the same meaning.

In which reference book would you

1. look for a synonym for a word? _____

2. find the greatest number of maps? _____

3. find information on how a dairy farm is run? _____

4. be most likely to find information on how much snow fell in each state last year? _____

5. look to find the pronunciation and meaning of a word?

   _____

6. look to find a list of the ten cities in the world that have the most people?

   _____

6 Book 4/Unit 2
Leah's Pony

At Home: Have students give examples of something they would research in each of the resources listed.

55

Cause and Effect

> In stories one thing often **causes** something else to happen. The result is an **effect**. As you read, look for what happens and why.

Read each story. Then write the missing cause or effect.

Mr. Bumper read an article that said "Fish food is brain food!" For four weeks he cooked fish each night. Though Mr. Bumper didn't feel any smarter, he was willing to continue this fish diet. However, Mr. Bumper finally stopped preparing fish. His family simply refused to keep eating fish every night.

1. Cause: Mr. Bumper thought that eating fish would make him smarter.

   Effect: _____

2. Cause: _____

   Effect: Mr. Bumper stopped making fish.

A magazine article said that doing a headstand for 10 minutes each day was good for a person's health. As a result, Mr. Andreas did a headstand each morning when he got to his office. After a month Mr. Andreas didn't feel much healthier. But now everyone in his company knew who he was. The company newsletter had printed a picture of Mr. Andreas standing on his head.

3. Cause: _____

   _____

   Effect: Mr. Andreas did a headstand each morning at his office.

4. Cause: A picture was printed that showed Mr. Andreas standing on his head.

   Effect: _____

   _____

At Home: Have students think of a famous person. Then have students think of causes for that fame.

Book 4/Unit 2
Leah's Pony 4

56

McGraw-Hill School Division

Sequence of Events

Sequence is the order in which things happen. Picturing the events in your mind often helps you understand the order in which events happen.

Each group of sentences below tells a story. The sentences are in the wrong order. Decide the correct order. Write the numbers 1 to 3 on the lines before the sentences to show the order in which events happened.

1. _____ Nora planted a garden.

   _____ Nora ordered seeds and got them through the mail.

   _____ Nora decided to plant a garden.

2. _____ Ed used his savings to buy a CD player.

   _____ Ed saved money from the movie theater paycheck.

   _____ The movie theater hired Ed to collect tickets.

3. _____ Yolanda started doing extra math homework every night.

   _____ Yolanda got low grades on two math tests in a row.

   _____ Yolanda's math grades improved.

4. _____ Ned used the note cards to give his speech.

   _____ Ned was asked to talk about his after-school computer business.

   _____ Ned put the major points of his speech on note cards.

Book 4/Unit 2
Leah's Pony
4

At Home: Have students list the steps in making a scrapbook.

57

Use Context Clues

When you read a word you don't know, look at the words and sentences around that word to learn its meaning. This is called using **context clues**.

Read each sentence. Circle the context clues that help you figure out the meaning of each underlined word. Then write the meaning on the line.

1. We work hard to put the cut hay into piles. The result is a field filled with

   haystacks. _____

2. Mr. Roth and his sons <u>toil</u> in the fields all day. This hard work keeps them

   fit. _____

3. Every fall, the farmers <u>harvest</u> their crops. After this gathering of the food,

   they have a celebration. _____

4. A century ago farmers used a horse to pull a <u>plow</u> through the field to turn up

   the soil for planting. _____

5. The cows are in the <u>pasture</u>. They eat in that grassy field until they

   are full. _____

6. The Beckley farm has pipes and sprinklers to water its crops. Many other

   farms use a similar system to <u>irrigate</u> their land. _____

At Home: Have students write a sentence with a context clue for the word *barn*.

Book 4/Unit 2
Leah's Pony 6

58

Make Predictions

| Reading titles can help you **predict** what a story will be about. |

Read each title. Then read the predictions of what the story will be about. Put a ✔ next to the prediction that makes the most sense.

1. "My Life on Stage"

_____ a history of movie theaters

_____ the life story of an actor

_____ the life story of an athlete

2. "To the Top!"

_____ mountain climbing

_____ toy making

_____ ocean exploration

3. "All Aboard: Travel on the Iron Tracks"

_____ a history of train travel

_____ a history of plane travel

_____ a history of the highway system

4. "Beneath the Waves"

_____ a man who flies a plane

_____ a man who explores caves

_____ a woman who explores the sea

5. "Causes for Celebration"

_____ math

_____ pet care

_____ holidays

5

Book 4/Unit 2
Baseball Saved Us

At Home: Choose the title of an unfamiliar story, book, or movie and have students predict what it will be about.

59

Vocabulary

Write a word from the list to complete each sentence.

crate	ditches	endless	glinting	inning	mound

1. The beach seemed _____ in length.

2. The field was surrounded by deep _____.

3. Sun was _____ off the water.

4. My uncle sent us a _____ that was full of oranges.

5. In the eighth _____, Mandy hit a home run.

6. The pitcher stood on the _____.

Story Comprehension

Write sentences to answer the questions about "Baseball Saved Us."

1. Why were the boy and his family sent to a government camp?

_____

2. Why did the boy's father decide to build a baseball field?

_____

_____

3. Why did the boy get angry with the guard in the tower?

_____

_____

4. After the boy got out of camp, how did baseball help the boy?

_____

_____

At Home: Have students use three of the vocabulary words to tell a story of their own.

60–61

Book 4/Unit 2
Baseball Saved Us

 4

McGraw-Hill School Division

Use an Encyclopedia

An **encyclopedia** is a set of books with articles about people, places, things, events, and ideas. The articles are arranged in alphabetical order in volumes.

Encyclopedia A 1	Encyclopedia B 2	Encyclopedia C-Ch 3	Encyclopedia Ci-Cz 4	Encyclopedia D 5	Encyclopedia E 6	Encyclopedia F 7	Encyclopedia G 8	Encyclopedia H 9	Encyclopedia I 10	Encyclopedia J-K 11	Encyclopedia L 12	Encyclopedia M 13	Encyclopedia N-O 14	Encyclopedia P 15	Encyclopedia Q-R 16	Encyclopedia S-Sn 17	Encyclopedia So-Sz 18	Encyclopedia T 19	Encyclopedia U-V 20	Encyclopedia W•X Y•Z 21	Research Guide & Index 22

Use the sample set of encyclopedias to answer these questions.
In which volume would you look for

1. an article on Japan? _____

2. more information on the city of Tokyo, Japan? _____

3. an article on the history of the United States? _____

4. information about Franklin Delano Roosevelt? _____

5. a picture of the Washington Monument? _____

What are three topics you would like to study? In which encyclopedia volumes would you find the information for your topic?

6. _____

7. _____

8. _____

Book 4/Unit 2 **Baseball Saved Us** 8

At Home: Have students try to find some of the information listed above in an encyclopedia at home or in the library.

62

McGraw-Hill School Division

Make Predictions

You can use clues from the story to help you **predict** what may happen next.

Read each story. Then answer the questions.

Emily had always been shy. But her shyness grew worse after her family moved. She tried to avoid talking to any of the people she met. Emily never raised her hand in class, and she walked straight home after school, alone.

Emily had been in school for five weeks and still had no friends. Then one day, she was sitting alone at a small lunch table, when she noticed three girls heading for her table.

1. What do you think Emily will do? _____

_____

2. Why? _____

_____

Felicia liked her home in town. But sometimes, she thought about the house by the sea. When she was a child, Felicia spent many happy summers there. Felicia had been heartbroken when her grandparents sold the house.

One day, Felicia saw that the house by the sea was for sale. She had saved enough money to allow her to buy it. She hadn't been planning to move. Yet, she felt happier than she'd been in months.

3. What do you think Felicia will decide to do? _____

_____

4. Why? _____

_____

At Home: Have students read the first paragraph of a story they choose and predict what will happen next.

Book 4/Unit 2
Baseball Saved Us
4

63

McGraw-Hill School Division

Form Generalizations

> A **generalization** is a broad statement based on a set of facts. Read the facts carefully. Decide what is true based on the facts.

Read each set of facts. Then complete each generalization.

The Steiner Group constructs buildings all over the state. It owns 13 office buildings and 13 shopping malls. The Group also owns 1 apartment building. The company has been in business for 26 years.

1. The Steiner group is a well known company that constructs buildings

_____.

2. The Steiner Group is a builder that has been respected by businesses

for _____.

Some people call Marina Del Sol a paradise. The daytime temperature is almost always between 70°F and 80°F, except in January and February. Then it is colder. Last month, there were only six days of rain. Most months, it rains less than that. If you want sunny days and a gentle ocean breeze, pack your bags and come to Marina Del Sol.

3. The daytime temperature in Marina Del Sol is almost never _____

_____.

4. In Marina Del Sol, rainy days _____

_____.

At Home: Have students list facts about the town in which they live and then make some generalizations.

Compound Words

A **compound word** is made up of two smaller words. You can usually figure out the meaning of the compound word by looking at the two smaller words and putting their meanings together.

Make a compound word by joining a word in the list to the end of one of the numbered words. Then write a sentence using the compound word.

brush	boat	pot	place	cloth	flake	coat	light

1. wash _____

_____

2. snow _____

_____

3. fire _____

_____

4. tooth _____

_____

5. moon _____

_____

6. motor _____

_____

7. rain _____

_____

8. flower _____

_____

At Home: Have students make compound words using each of the following words: horse, horn, shoe, fog.

65

Book 4/Unit 2
Baseball Saved Us 8

McGraw-Hill School Division

Cause and Effect

> Noting **cause** and **effect** relationships as you read will help you better understand and enjoy the selection.

Read the story. Then fill in the missing causes and effects in the chart.

> Almost every day, Richard rode his horse around the edge of his ranch. Two months ago, Richard found a stray dog sleeping near the back gate. Someone had left the gate open by mistake.
>
> The dog had no tags. Richard called his neighbors and the local sheriff. None of them knew about any dogs that were missing. So, Richard decided to take care of the dog himself.
>
> At first, the dog was very weak. He must have been wandering for days without food. But Richard fed the dog and slowly the dog recovered. After a few weeks, the dog was running around and chasing birds. Richard decided to name the dog Birdman.

Effect, or what happened	Cause, or why it happened
1. _____ _____	Someone left the back gate open by mistake.
2. _____ _____	Richard wanted to find out who the dog belonged to.
3. Richard decided to take care of the dog himself.	_____ _____
4. The dog became very weak.	_____ _____
5. Richard decided to name the dog Birdman.	_____

Book 4/Unit 2
Will Her Native Language Disappear?
5

At Home: Have students identify some effects of a storm, such as a hurricane or tornado.

66

McGraw-Hill School Division

Vocabulary

Choose the word that matches the meaning. Then fill in the crossword puzzle.

communicate	**extinct**	**native**
backgrounds	**generations**	**century**

Across

2. exchange information; make known
4. gone; dead
5. experiences; environments

Down

1. stages in family history
2. period of 100 years
3. relating to a certain person or place

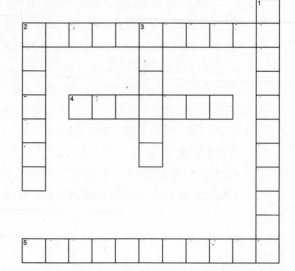

Story Comprehension

Write **True** or **False** next to each statement about "Will Her Native Language Disappear?" Look back at the article for help.

1. _____ Not being able to communicate makes people lonely.

2. _____ All Native American children speak their native languages.

3. _____ Some people still speak Choctaw.

4. _____ Languages can become endangered or extinct.

5. _____ Many young people do not value their native language.

6. _____ The Endangered Language Fund prints books in languages that are dying out.

At Home: Have students write a short story using at least four vocabulary words.

Book 4/Unit 2
Will Her Native Language Disappear? 6

Conduct an Interview

> The purpose of an **interview** is to gather information about a person. The person who asks the questions is the *interviewer*. The person who answers the questions is the *interviewee*.

Below are some words to remember when preparing to interview someone.

> **Key Words for Conducting an Interview:**
> **Purpose**—Know It
> **Prepare**
> **Questions:** *Who? What? Where? When? Why? How?*
> **Listen**
> **Take Notes**

A famous Olympic skating champion is coming to your school. You have been chosen to interview her at a school assembly. Answer the following questions about your interview with the champion.

1. How would you begin the interview? _____

_____

_____

2. What would be the purpose of the interview? _____

_____

_____

3. Write three questions you could ask in the interview. _____

_____

_____

4. If the skater mentions the jumps and turns she does, but you don't understand

the skating terms, what should you do? _____

_____

_____

McGraw-Hill School Division

At Home: Have students think of someone they would like to interview, and then have them write four questions for the interview.

Form Generalizations

> Often when you read you can make a **generalization**, or a broad statement, about facts you are given.

Read the paragraphs below. Put a ✔ next to generalizations you can make based on what you read.

At Monk Street Mini Mall, you can shop at Just Pants, the Coat Factory, Socks Ahoy, Completely Clothing, Sam's Sportswear, and Mega Jeans. You can also go to The Bagel Shack or to Cone City. Next to Cone City is Main Bank's automated teller machine.

1. _____ There are not many choices of food at Monk Street Mini Mall.

2. _____ The mini mall has no banking services.

3. _____ Most of the stores at the mini mall sell clothes.

On Monday and Wednesday afternoons, Nadine has piano lessons. On Thursday afternoon, she sings in a choir. On Friday, Saturday, and Sunday, Nadine practices piano at least two hours a day. Tuesday afternoon, Nadine has tennis lessons.

4. _____ Nadine spends no time on sports.

5. _____ Music is a big part of Nadine's life.

6. _____ Nadine's mother forces her to take music lessons.

At Home: Have students tell why items 2, 4, and 6 are not valid generalizations.

70

Book 4/Unit 2
Will Her Native Language Disappear?   6

Compound Words

When two words are put together to make one word, the new word is called a **compound word**.

Circle the compound word in each sentence. Write the two words that make up each compound word. Then write the meaning of the compound word.

1. We have the largest classroom in the school.

Word parts: _____ + _____

Meaning: _____

2. Rosita went on safari to see wildlife in its own environment.

Word parts: _____ + _____

Meaning: _____

3. The steamboat was an important invention.

Word parts: _____ + _____

Meaning: _____

4. Ken had to work in the barnyard every Saturday.

Word parts: _____ + _____

Meaning: _____

5. Juan put a mousetrap in the cellar.

Word parts: _____ + _____

Meaning: _____

10 Book 4/Unit 2
Will Her Native Language Disappear?

At Home: Ask students if carpet and father are compound words. Why or why not?

71

Use Context Clues

> When you read a word you don't know, look at the words and sentences near that word. This is called using **context clues**.

Circle the letter beside the meaning of the underlined word in each sentence.

1. There is a <u>hammock</u> hung between two trees in the backyard. Try it for a nap.

    a. a swinging bed made of cloth   **b.** a sports net

2. In the winter, some Inuit people lived in <u>igloos</u>. They formed the dome-shaped huts from packed snow.

    a. special animal traps   **b.** shelters

3. The family owned a large <u>hacienda</u> where they raised cattle.

    a. a ranch   **b.** a campground

4. I slip on my <u>moccasins</u> when I get home. They comfort my feet.

    a. indoor slipper or shoe   **b.** warm vest

5. Some Native Americans lived in <u>wigwams</u>. They made these by covering poles with hides or bark.

    a. places to live   **b.** means of travel

6. The long flat design of a <u>toboggan</u> makes it great for riding down snow-covered hills.

    a. a type of boat   **b.** a type of sled

At Home: Have students identify the context clues they used to help them decide the meaning of *hacienda* and *igloos*.

72

Book 4/Unit 2
Will Her Native Language Disappear?
6

Unit 2 Vocabulary Review

A. Write the correct word from the list.

native	glinting	lingered	crumpled

1. Claudia _____ in her seat long after the play was over.

2. Joel _____ the wrapper and threw it in the garbage.

3. Light was _____ off the metal on the building.

4. French is Sabine's _____ language.

B. Read each question. Choose a word from the list to answer the question. Write your answer on the line.

county	mound	guilt	foul

1. How might you describe something that smells bad? _____

2. What word names a part of a state? _____

3. What might you feel when you do something wrong? _____

4. What is something that a baseball pitcher stands on? _____

At Home: Have students look for these vocabulary words in magazines and copy the sentences in which the words appear.

Unit 2 Vocabulary Review

A. Use the words from the list to complete the crossword puzzle.

| inning | clustered | bulging | haze | extinct | crate |

Across

3. grouped together

5. wooden box

6. part of a baseball game

Down

1. smoke or dust in the air

2. swelling outwards

4. dead; gone

B. Write the correct word from the list.

| century | endless | overflowing | shrieking |

The stadium was **1.** _____ with fans. The

newspapers had called this the game of the **2.** _____.

When the players came on the gigantic field, the fans began

3. _____. The noise seemed as if it would be

4. _____.

At Home: Have students use three of the vocabulary words on this page to write a scary story.

74

Book 4/Unit 2
Unit 2 Vocabulary Review 10

Make Judgments and Decisions

> **Making judgments and decisions** is a natural part of storytelling and story reading. When you read a story you read about characters who think about what they will do in difficult situations. As a reader, you too, can think about what you may do in similar situations.

Read the story. Then answer the questions.

Lucinda was excited as she finished writing her story. She thought she had a good chance to win the story contest. She had read the rules carefully, and had thought a lot about what her story was going to be about. Then she had written it, choosing her words carefully. When she finished writing the story she read it and thought it was great. Then she showed it to her best friend, Pam. Pam told her to change several things about the story to make it different. Lucinda liked Pam, but was confused by her advice.

1. What decision does Lucinda have to make?

_____

_____

2. What things should Lucinda think about before she makes a decision?

_____

_____

_____

3. Suppose you were Lucinda. What might you say to Pam?

_____

4. Who else might help Lucinda decide what to do?

_____

4
Book 4/Unit 3
The Hatmaker's Sign

At Home: Have students discuss a decision they have made and how they came to it.

75

Vocabulary

Read each clue. Then find the vocabulary word in the row of letters and circle it.

admitted	brisk	displaying	elegantly	strolling	wharf

1. quick   n b r i s k d a q t e c f

2. richly or beautifully   p r w s c e l e g a n t l y i

3. showing   t r v m d i s p l a y i n g f e

4. confessed   w u n a d m i t t e d k o l

5. landing place for boats   a l d p i r w h a r f k n d s

6. walking slowly and in a   l e s t r o l l i n g r c b n k
relaxed way

6

Story Comprehension

Write a complete sentence to answer each question about "The Hatmaker's Sign."

1. Who is the main character of the story?

_____

2. How did the hatmaker feel about his sign before he talked to others?

_____

3. How did everyone want him to change the sign?

_____

4. What did the sign maker suggest about changing the sign?

_____

5. Why did Ben Franklin share this story with Jefferson?

_____

_____

At Home: Have students retell the main events of "The Hatmaker's Sign."

76–77

Book 4/Unit 3
The Hatmaker's Sign 5

McGraw-Hill School Division

Read Signs

Signs are all around us. Many signs use symbols to tell us things in a short, quick way. These kinds of signs have simple drawings that stand for actions, objects, or directions.

Read the signs. Draw a line from each sign to the correct meaning.

1.    slippery road

2.    Exit

3.    disabled access

4.    telephone

5.    school crossing

Book 4/Unit 3
The Hatmaker's Sign
5

At Home: Have students look for signs around their school and discuss their meanings.

78

Make Judgments and Decisions

> It is common for readers to put themselves in the place of a character in a story. Readers who do this **make judgments and decisions** about the characters and their actions.

Read the story. Then answer the questions.

Luis was looking forward to playing soccer with his team on the weekend. He was also happy because on the playground, his friend Larry had talked about having the whole group over some time. Larry's family lived on the lake and had a big boat.

Luis had a problem, though. Larry had invited everyone to the lake on the same weekend as the game. Luis knew the team should come first. But, Lester, a friend, said if Luis didn't go to the lake, Larry would be angry and would never invite him again.

1. What should Luis do? _____

_____

_____

2. Should Luis listen to Lester's advice? Why? _____

_____

_____

3. If you were Luis, what would you say to Larry? _____

_____

_____

_____

4. If you were Luis and others made fun of your decision to play the game, how

would you feel? _____

_____

_____

At Home: Have students comment on a judgment or decision made by a television show character.

Book 4/Unit 3
The Hatmaker's Sign 4

79

McGraw-Hill School Division

Summarize

When you **summarize**, you tell the most important parts of something you have read. Include the main idea and only important details.

Read the selection. Then answer the questions.

Thomas Jefferson was a talented and respected man. He is most famous for writing The Declaration of Independence, but he also served as the third President of the United States.

Jefferson was a shy man who preferred reading and studying to being with groups of people. He was a scientist, inventor, and builder. His home in Virginia is studied as an example of beautiful architecture. Jefferson also founded the University of Virginia in his home state. In his time, Jefferson was very important in the United States. People looked up to him and asked his advice on many matters of importance.

1. What is the main idea? _____

_____

2. What is Jefferson most famous for? _____

_____

3. What else was Jefferson famous for? _____

_____

_____

4. How would you summarize the selection? _____

_____

_____

_____

Suffixes

> **Suffixes** are word endings. They add to the meaning of a word. The suffix *-ful* adds the meaning "full of" to a word.

Add the suffix *-ful* to each word.

1. fear + ful = _____
2. help + ful = _____
3. hope + ful = _____
4. joy + ful = _____
5. doubt + ful = _____
6. health + ful = _____

Now use one of the words above with *-ful* to complete each sentence.

7. Carrot sticks are a _____ snack.
8. She was _____ that she could finish on time.
9. My brother is _____ of dark places.
10. Birthdays are _____ occasions.
11. Can you be _____ and hand me the hammer?
12. Aaron is _____ he will win the contest.

At Home: Have students use three words they formed in sentences of their own.

Book 4/Unit 3
The Hatmaker's Sign

81

12

Fact and Opinion

A **fact** is a statement that can be proven in some way. An **opinion** is a statement of a person's belief that may not be able to be proven.

Read each story. Then write examples of facts or opinions from the story.

In the United States, there are three branches of government. The legislative branch is the Congress, which is made up of the Senate and the House of Representatives. The judicial branch is headed by the Supreme Court. The executive branch is headed by the President. This three-part system of government is the best in the world because no one branch has total power.

1. Write two facts. _____

_____

_____

2. Write one opinion. _____

_____

There are over 200 bones in the human body. The bones are joined together to make a skeleton. The bones help us stand and protect organs like the heart, lungs, and brain. Ben is convinced that his bones are unbreakable.

3. Write two facts. _____

_____

_____

4. Write one opinion. _____

_____

Book 4/Unit 3
Pat Cummings: My Story
4

At Home: Have students read an article in the newspaper and identify one fact and one opinion.

82

Vocabulary

Complete each definition by writing the correct word on the line provided.

exist	image	inspire	loft	reference	sketch

1. A large room or open space on the upper floor of a building is a

   _____.

2. A picture of something in the mind is an _____.

3. To make a quick drawing is to _____.

4. Something used for information is a _____.

5. To stir the imagination is to _____.

6. To live is to _____.

Story Comprehension

Write the answers to these questions about "Pat Cummings: My Story." For help, you can look back at the story.

1. What was the first thing Pat Cummings drew that people could recognize?

   _____

2. Where does Pat Cummings get her ideas? _____

   _____

3. What does Pat Cummings like to draw? _____

   _____

4. How does Pat Cummings go about drawing people? _____

   _____

5. How did Tom Feelings inspire Cummings? _____

   _____

   _____

At Home: Have students make a simple crossword puzzle using some of the vocabulary words.

Book 4/Unit 3
Pat Cummings: My Story   5

83–84

Read a Flowchart

A **flowchart** is a chart or diagram that tells you how to do something step-by-step.

How to Hold a School Art Show

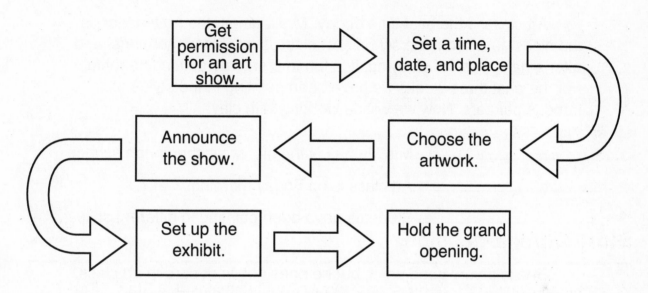

Use the flowchart to answer the questions.

1. What does this flowchart show? _____

_____

2. What is the first step? _____

3. What is the next step? _____

_____

4. At which step do you announce the show? _____

5. What is the last step in producing the art show? _____

_____

At Home: Have students make their own flowchart of the steps it takes to do something familiar, such as make a sandwich.

Fact and Opinion

> As you read, it is important to be able to tell what are facts and what are opinions. **Facts** can be proven. **Opinions** cannot.

Read each paragraph. Then write whether each numbered statement is a fact or an opinion.

Art class is the best time of day. Mrs. James, the art teacher, is the nicest teacher in the school. Art class is on Friday mornings, and after a hard week of studying, it is fun to create something beautiful. For the past three weeks we have been painting in the styles of famous painters. Now we will be working with clay.

1. _____ Mrs. James is the nicest teacher in the school.

2. _____ Art class is on Friday mornings.

3. _____ Students have been painting in different styles.

Ben is a very good artist, but he does not work hard in art class. He hates to draw still lifes, and even tore up his last art class drawing. Michael sat next to Ben at lunch. When Ben opened his notebook, Michael saw that it was covered with cartoons and funny little drawings. Michael thinks that Ben's cartoons are pretty good.

4. _____ Ben tore up his drawing.

5. _____ Ben's notebook is covered with cartoons.

6. _____ Michael thinks that Ben's cartoons are pretty good.

At Home: Have students state two facts and two opinions about their favorite class at school.

Book 4/Unit 3
Pat Cummings: My Story 6

86

Summarize

> When you **summarize**, you should include the main idea and the most important details from what you read.

Read the selection. Circle the letter beside the best response to each question.

> Anna Mary Moses was an artist who never went to art school. She spent most of her life as a wife and mother of ten children. When she was 78 years of age, "Grandma" Moses took up painting. She sold her first painting for $3.
>
> During the following years she painted over 1,500 pictures. They were mainly scenes of country life. Anna Mary Moses continued painting until just before her death at the age of 101. Today, Grandma Moses is thought of as an important American artist. Her paintings are in many museums.

1. Which is the main idea?

   a. Grandma Moses became an artist at the age of 78.

   b. Grandma Moses died at the age of 101.

2. Which detail is more important?

   a. Grandma Moses had ten children.

   b. Grandma Moses never went to art school.

3. Which detail is more important?

   a. Grandma Moses once sold a painting for $3.

   b. Grandma Moses painted scenes of country life.

4. Which is the better way to summarize the paragraph?

   a. Grandma Moses, an important American artist, began to paint late in life. She had no art training but painted over 1,500 pictures of rural scenes.

   b. Grandma Moses was a mother and a painter. She painted rural scenes. She once sold a painting for $3.

Book 4/Unit 3
Pat Cummings: My Story

At Home: Have students summarize their day at school, including the main idea and important details.

4

Suffixes

A **suffix** is a word part that adds meaning to a word. The suffixes *-ful* and *-ous* add the meaning "full of" or "having."

Add the suffix *-ful* or *-ous* to each word.

1. danger   +   ous   = _____
2. play   +   ful   = _____
3. courage   +   ous   = _____
4. humor   +   ous   = _____
5. sorrow   +   ful   = _____
6. glamour   +   ous   = _____

Now use one of the words above with *-ful* or *-ous* to complete each sentence.

7. The comic told _____ stories.
8. It is _____ to play with matches.
9. Jena felt _____ when her friend moved.
10. Firefighters are _____ citizens.
11. Kittens and puppies are active and _____.
12. She looked _____ in the gown.

At Home: Have students identify one more *-ful* and one more *-ous* suffixed word.

Book 4/Unit 3
Pat Cummings: My Story 12

88

McGraw-Hill School Division

Author's Purpose and Point of View

> An author writes with one or more **purposes**—to entertain, to teach or inform, or to persuade. An author also reveals his or her **point of view** on a subject by the way he or she writes about it.

Read each paragraph. Circle the letter beside the best answer to each question.

Three strangers met on the road. They were all going to the village. Under a tree they saw a pile of gold coins. Two strangers filled their pockets. The third stranger said it would not be right to take the gold. At the village, the strangers separated. The two with the gold had great misfortunes in days to come. The third man had nothing but days of golden happiness to reward his just behavior.

1. What is the author's purpose?

   a. to persuade

   b. to teach

2. Thinking about the point of view in the paragraph, what do you think the author would do if he or she found a wallet on the street?

   a. keep it and what was inside

   b. try to return it

   Citizens should exercise their right to vote. It is more important to vote than it is to vote for a particular candidate. So, cast your vote as you see fit. I am going to vote for Robert Martin. He is the candidate who has supported fair and honest government.

3. What is the author's purpose?

   a. to persuade

   b. to entertain

4. What does the author believe?

   a. Citizens should vote.

   b. Government is not for everyone.

McGraw-Hill School Division

Book 4/Unit 3
Grass Sandals
4

At Home: Have students choose a newspaper article and tell the author's purpose.

Vocabulary

Choose a word from the list to complete each sentence.

chanted	nipped	pouch	restless	scribbled	stitching

1. The child _____ with a crayon.

2. The puppy _____ at the little girl's heels.

3. The choir _____ words as the music played.

4. The boy was _____ and wanted to play outside.

5. My Mom is _____ the hole in my jeans.

6. The hiker carried supplies in a waterproof _____.

Story Comprehension

Write the answers to these questions about "Grass Sandals." You can refer to the story for help if you need to.

1. When and where did Basho live? _____

_____

2. What did Basho promise his hat? _____

_____

3. Where did Basho begin his journey? _____

_____

4. What did Basho write about? _____

_____

5. Why is Basho known and loved in Japan? _____

_____

At Home: Have students recall their favorite part of Basho's journey.

90–91

Book 4/Unit 3
Grass Sandals 5

Read a Map

CALIFORNIA

Sacramento

San Francisco

Pacific Ocean

Mt. Whitney

Mojave Desert

Los Angeles

San Diego

Read the map to answer the questions.

1. What are three large cities on California's Pacific Ocean? _____

2. Which city on the map is farthest from the Pacific Ocean? _____

_____

3. Which city is closest to the Mojave Desert? _____

_____

4. If you traveled from San Francisco to Los Angeles, in what direction would you be heading? _____

_____

5. Which cities would you expect to trade with countries across the Pacific Ocean? Why? _____

_____

5 | Book 4/Unit 3
Grass Sandals

At Home: Have students look at a map and name the capital and one other large city in their state.

92

Author's Purpose and Point of View

> Authors often write to entertain or to persuade. These are their **purposes**. They often express **their point of view** about a subject through characters and story events.

Read each story. Then circle the letter beside the best response.

Julie and Andres enjoy hiking. They also enjoy biking along trails. In fact, it seems they take every opportunity to be outdoors. The mountain air and the woodsy smell of the forest make them feel happy and healthy. It makes them sad to see garbage left by people in natural areas. Together they have written letters to make stricter laws against littering.

1. Which would the author favor?

   a. indoor activities   **b.** outdoor activities

2. How would he or she vote on stricter laws against littering?

   a. He or she would vote no.   **b.** He or she would vote yes.

"Never!" shouted Sean. "I won't do it. Greasy fries, cold burgers, and little chicken parts are not real food. I prefer salads and fruit, and maybe some cheese. There are only empty calories in what they sell at this Snack Shack."

3. How does the author feel about fast food?

   a. The author probably likes it.   **b.** He or she probably never eats it.

4. Which cause might the author support?

   a. Veggies in the schools   **b.** National Corn Dog Day

At Home: Have students explain why they chose the responses they chose for the above paragraphs.

93

Book 4/Unit 3
Grass Sandals   4

Make Judgments and Decisions

Characters in a story often face difficult situations in which they must decide what to do. Readers often think about what they might do if they were in similar situations. This is called **making judgments and decisions**.

Read the story. Then answer the questions.

Jesse was excited about visiting his young cousin Sherry. Despite their age differences and the fact that Sherry was a girl, they had many things in common. Like Jesse, Sherry loved chess, reading, and action movies. So when Jesse saw one of his favorite videos on sale, he bought it as a gift for Sherry. His mom, whom he met at the Food Court, did not approve. "That is not a good gift for someone who already sits in front of the television too much," she said sternly.

Jesse's big sister came over and whispered in his ear, "What a nice thing to do. Sherry will love it."

1. Why did Jesse decide to get the video? _____

_____

2. Why do you think Jesse's mom is against the gift? _____

_____

_____

3. If you were Jesse, what would you do—return the gift and choose something

else or give it to Sherry anyway? Why? _____

_____

_____

4. If Jesse asked you for advice, what would you tell him? _____

_____

_____

_____

4 Book 4/Unit 3
Grass Sandals

At Home: Have students think about a decision they made during the day and explain why they decided what they did.

94

Context Clues

When you come across words you don't know, many times you can figure out their meaning from the **context**. The words in the sentence, or the sentences before and after the word, can give you clues as to what the word means.

Read the paragraph. Circle the letter beside the meaning of each of the numbered words. Then write the clues in the paragraph that helped you figure out the meaning.

America was settled by pioneers. These courageous, early settlers traveled west despite danger and obstacles such as waterfalls, rivers, and mountains. They had to transport their canoes around waterfalls, lifting boats over steep rocks. They had to ford wide rivers in wagons pulled by oxen and guide horses along steep mountain cliffs and dry, rocky ground.

1. pioneers

    a. early explorers   **b.** last to arrive

    Clues: _____

2. obstacles

    a. easy passageways   **b.** things in the way

    Clues: _____

3. transport

    a. carry from place to place   **b.** hold in place

    Clues: _____

4. ford

    a. to bypass   **b.** to cross

    Clues: _____

McGraw-Hill School Division

At Home: Have students use two words from the exercise in sentences.

Book 4/Unit 3
Grass Sandals 4

95

Fact and Opinion

> A **fact** is a statement that can be proven in some way. An **opinion** is a statement of someone's belief that cannot always be proven.

Read each paragraph. Write **F** if the statement is a fact. Write **O** if it is an opinion.

From the first days of their settlement, Europeans came to what is now the United States and moved inland from the coasts. I think moving is bad for children. My family has moved three times and I am only nine years old. But pioneer families used to move often. They would clear the land, stay a while, and then move on again when the area became crowded or the soil grew poor. I think the children in those families did not like moving. I hope we stay here for a long time.

1. I think moving is bad for kids. _____

2. People came to what is now the United States and moved inland from the

   coasts. _____

3. I hope we stay here for a long time. _____

4. My family has moved three times. _____

5. I think the children in those families did not like moving. _____

I like riding on trains. I really like the clickety-clack sound the train makes on the rails. My mom rides the train to work. She takes the same train every morning. I go to work with her sometimes. I love getting on the train early in the morning.

6. I like riding on trains. _____

7. The train makes a clickety-clack sound on the rails. _____

8. My mom rides the train to work. _____

Book 4/Unit 3
A Place Called Freedom
8

At Home: Have students find three facts and three opinions in a magazine article.

96

Vocabulary

Write a word from the list to complete each sentence.

fretted	gourd	plantation	settlement	sunrise	weary

1. A large farm or estate that grows a single crop was called a

_____.

2. If you stayed up all night and saw the sky grow light, you would see the

_____.

3. Another word for *worried* is _____.

4. A dried fruit shell sometimes used for drinking is a _____.

5. Another word for *tired* is _____.

6. A small village or group of houses is called a _____.

Reteach 98

Story Comprehension

Write a ✔ next to every sentence that tells about "A Place Called Freedom." For help you may look back at the story.

1. _____The author and his family left Tennessee for Indiana.

2. _____Starman had been the plantation owner's name.

3. _____The Starman family bought land near the Wabash River.

4. _____Papa was not able to bring any relatives to Indiana.

5. _____Other people who had escaped from slavery came to the settlement to live.

6. _____Papa and Mama wanted to name the village Starman.

7. _____The new town was named Freedom.

8. _____The narrator became a farmer like his father and a teacher like his mother.

At Home: Have students write a paragraph retelling the events in "A Place Called Freedom" in their own words.

Book 4/Unit 3
A Place Called Freedom 8

97–98

McGraw-Hill School Division

Read a Line Graph

Graphs of all kinds give information in a shorthand way. A **line graph** shows how a piece of information changes with time. It would take many words to describe the same changes you might "read" about in a graph.

Population of Libertyville

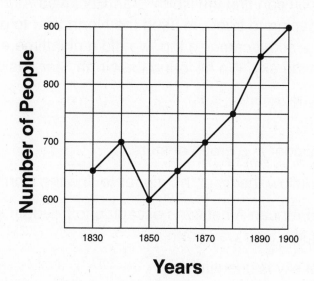

Use the line graph to answer the questions.

1. What was the population of Libertyville in 1850? _____

2. Compare the population of the year 1830 to 1860. Was the population in 1860 higher, lower, or the same as in 1830? _____

3. Which year had the lowest population? _____

4. Which years had the greatest population growth? _____

5. Which years had the greatest loss in population? _____

5 Book 4/Unit 3
A Place Called Freedom

At Home: Have students make a line graph to record personal information, such as how much they save or spend month by month for a year or half year.

99

Fact and Opinion

Knowing that a **fact** is a statement that can be proven to be true and that an **opinion** is someone's personal belief can help you understand what you read.

Read the paragraph. Write **F** if the statement is a fact. Write **O** if the statement is an opinion.

> The big dipper is my favorite group of stars. If you follow the tip of the dipper, you can find the North Star. Enslaved African Americans escaping to freedom used the North Star to guide their way north. On a scout camping trip, we did a nighttime exercise finding stars in the sky. We all found the North Star easily in the beautiful sky.

1. _____The big dipper is a group of stars.

2. _____You can follow the tip of the dipper to find the North Star.

3. _____Enslaved African Americans escaping to freedom used the North Star to guide their way north.

4. _____The night sky is beautiful.

Now you try. Write two facts and then write two opinions about pies.

5. Fact: _____

6. Fact: _____

7. Opinion: _____

8. Opinion: _____

At Home: Have students express their opinions about news events.

Book 4/Unit 3
A Place Called Freedom 8

100

McGraw-Hill School Division

Summarize

> If you can **summarize** a story well, you can be sure that you have understood the most important parts of the story.

Read the paragraph and then answer the questions.

Mr. LeTour's house was flooded when the creek spilled over its banks. He needed help cleaning his collection of old baseball cards. My Dad says it is very valuable. Mr. LeTour had wrapped each card in a clear plastic envelope. The envelopes had kept the cards dry during the flood, but now the envelopes were covered with mud. He hired Carrie McCourt and me to clean them. All weekend long, we worked with rags dipped in a special cleaner. Mr. LeTour was a lot happier on Sunday when he saw his sparkling clean envelopes.

1. What is the main idea of the story? _____

_____

_____

2. Who are the characters in the story? _____

_____

3. What is the story problem and its solution? _____

_____

_____

4. Use your answers above to summarize the story. _____

_____

_____

_____

Context Clues

Use **context clues,** or other words and sentences in the text, to help you figure out an unfamiliar word.

Read the paragraph. Then circle the letter beside the meaning of each of the words listed below. Next tell which clues in the paragraph helped you figure out the meanings.

My grandfather loved to recount our family stories. He told again and again about his great-grandmother and other ancestors who escaped from slavery. I liked the part about how they had to improvise when the slave catchers came upon them suddenly. That's where we get the ability to solve things quickly, my grandfather told me. Grandpa always said that enslaved people who were fugitives from the law and made it to freedom had to be smart.

1. recount

　a. repeat

　　　　　　　　　　　　b. keep secret

Clues: _____

2. ancestors

　a. family member who lived before you

　　　　　　　　　　　　b. family friends

Clues: _____

3. improvise

　a. practice ahead of time

　　　　　　　　　　　　b. do something without planning

Clues: _____

4. fugitives

　a. runaways

　　　　　　　　　　　　b. officers

Clues: _____

At Home: Have students find a word they don't know in a story and give its meaning from context clues.

Book 4/Unit 3
A Place Called Freedom

102

McGraw-Hill School Division

Make Judgments and Decisions

> **Making judgments and decisions** is a natural part of storytelling and story reading. Characters must think about what they will do in difficult situations. Readers must think about what they might do in similar situations.

Read the story. Then write an answer to each question.

Mickey got off the bus. He stood still and stared straight ahead. He could see the building where the department store was. It was only about a half block away. This was the first time his dad had let him come downtown by himself to buy his own clothes. Now he almost wished his dad had come along. Mickey pictured the big store, the crowds, and the many choices he would have. Suddenly he didn't feel very well. He saw the bus that was headed back to his home, and he got a wild idea.

1. What decision does Mickey have to make? _____

_____

_____

2. Why did his dad decide to let him go downtown alone? _____

_____

_____

3. Why does Mickey wish his dad had come along? _____

_____

_____

4. If you were Mickey, what would you do? _____

_____

_____

McGraw-Hill School Division

Book 4/Unit 3
Twisted Trails
4

At Home: Have students tell what they would say to Mickey if he had skipped his trip to the store.

103

Vocabulary

Use the correct word from the list.

challenge	contained	combine	entertaining	mazes	requires

1. The _____ were like life-size puzzles.

2. It is a real _____ to try to find your way through a maze.

3. To find your way through a maze, you need to _____ a sense of direction and a good memory.

4. Finding your way through a maze also _____ paying attention to details.

5. My favorite maze _____ many twisting paths.

6. It is _____ to walk through a maze.

☐/6

Story Comprehension

Write an answer to each question about "Twisted Trails."

1. Who is Adrian Fisher? _____

_____

2. What kinds of skills does he need to design mazes? _____

_____

3. Why do people like corn mazes? _____

_____

4. In what state is there a museum that has shown Fisher's mazes? _____

_____

At Home: Have students tell about the article "Twisted Trails"

104–105

Book 4/Unit 3
Twisted Trails

☐/4

McGraw-Hill School Division

Read a Diagram

> A **diagram** is a plan or a drawing. One kind of diagram shows the arrangement of things in a place.

Library / Floor 1

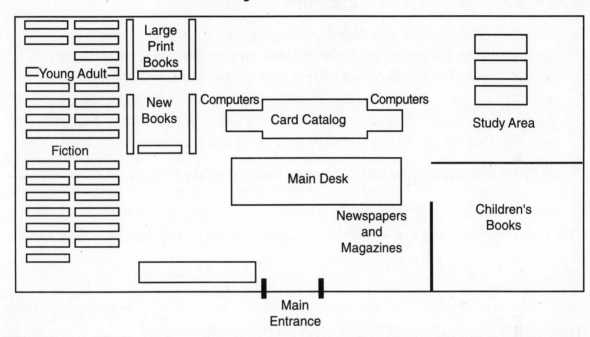

One place to find out more about mazes is in the library.
Use the diagram of the library to answer the questions.

1. Where is the card catalog located? _____

2. In the diagram, what is to the right of the newspapers and magazines?

   _____

3. What is just in front of the card catalog? _____

4. What is just behind the children's books? _____

Book 4/Unit 3
Twisted Trails
4

At Home: Have students draw a diagram of their classroom or school cafeteria.

106

Author's Purpose and Point of View

Authors often let readers know how they feel about a subject through the characters and situations they choose to write about. They express their **point of view** through their stories.

Read the story. Then answer the questions.

> Some neighbors say that the prairie can be seen on Sara's face. Some admire her strength. Others feel sorry for her. In winter, Sara is pale, almost gray. She looks tired and cold like the snowy flat land around her. In summer, Sara is sunburned and seems always to be thirsty. No amount of water can take away the dryness of her hair or skin. To look at Sara is to know what life on the prairie is like.

1. What does the author use the character Sara to really talk about? _____

_____

2. Does the author think the prairie is an easy place to live? Tell how you know?

_____

_____

3. Do you think the author has ever lived on the prairie? Why? _____

_____

4. Do you think the author admires Sara or feels sorry for her? Why?

_____

_____

_____

_____

_____

At Home: Have students reread a favorite story to see if they can tell how the author feels about a subject.

Book 4/Unit 3
Twisted Trails 4

107

McGraw-Hill School Division

Context Clues

> Good readers use **context clues** to help them figure out unfamiliar words.

Read the paragraph. Circle the letter giving the meaning of each of the words listed below. Then tell what clues in the paragraph helped you.

> In the construction business there are lots of people who need to work together. Putting up big buildings is a complicated job. The architect draws the plans for the building. Architects need to consult with engineers who are the experts on how to build. Lawyers have to deal with legal matters. Someone has to set up the schedule to make sure things get done at the right time.

1. complicated

   a. simple to do   **b.** hard to do

   Clues: _____

   _____

2. consult

   a. disagree with   **b.** talk together about

   Clues: _____

   _____

3. legal

   a. relating to money   **b.** relating to the law

   Clues: _____

   _____

4. schedule

   a. time plan   **b.** list of workers

   Clues: _____

   _____

Book 4/Unit 3
Twisted Trails
4

At Home: Have students use the numbered words in sentences of their own.

108

Suffixes

> Knowing the meaning a **suffix** adds to a word can help you read and understand unfamiliar words. The suffixes -*ful* and *ous* add the meaning "full of" or "having" to words.

Read the list of words with suffixes. Think about the meaning of each word. Then write a word to complete each sentence.

hazardous	**restful**	**famous**	**pitiful**
careful	**healthful**	**disastrous**	**thoughtful**

1. Fast food does not make a _____ meal.

2. We spent a _____ afternoon lying on the beach.

3. The student looked _____ when questioned by his teacher.

4. Some bug sprays are _____ to the environment.

5. The _____ movie star signed my autograph book.

6. The shipwreck was a _____ accident.

7. The sick parrot gave a _____ cry.

8. It's important to be _____ when you light the candles.

At Home: Have students explain the spelling changes needed to form famous disastrous, and pitiful.

109

Book 4/Unit 3
Twisted Trails

8

Unit 3 Vocabulary Review

A. Write a word from the list to complete each sentence.

sunrise	brisk	entertaining	weary	strolling	mazes

1. Louie went for a _____ walk.

2. He came across Denise _____ through the park.

3. We got up before _____.

4. It is no surprise that we were _____ by afternoon.

5. We walked through the _____.

6. It was an _____ afternoon.

B. Read each clue. Then find the vocabulary word from the list in the row of letters and circle it.

displaying	wharf	fretted	exist

1. worried   m a f r e t t e d y u d a w

2. showing   l k a s n d i s p l a y i n g a f

3. to live   o j f e x i s t r g v s q a

4. boat landing m r o j w h a r f n c v

At Home: Have students use three vocabulary words in sentences of their own.

Unit 3 Vocabulary Review

A. Read each question. Then write a word from the list to answer each question.

chanted	sketch	loft	plantation	pouch

1. If you were to draw quickly, what would you do? _____

2. What was a large farm that usually grew one crop called? _____

3. What is a small bag or sack called? _____

4. What might the choir have done as the organ played? _____

5. What is a large room or open space on the upper floor of a building called?

_____

B. Write a word from the list to complete each sentence.

reference	inspire	restless	challenge	image

1. I was so excited I couldn't sit still. After a while, Mom asked why I was so

_____.

2. Older kids help me learn. They _____ me.

3. She often uses her state almanac as a _____.

4. Aunt Bertha stared at little Carrie. She was the _____ of

her mother.

5. The book was 300 pages long. It was a _____, but I read it all.

At Home: Encourage students to use the vocabulary words in their personal writing.

111

Book 4/Unit 3
Unit 3 Vocabulary Review
10

Compare and Contrast

> When you **compare and contrast**, you tell how two or more things are alike and different.

Read each paragraph. Then write an **X** next to each true sentence that states how two characters are alike or different.

Nora and Cora are identical twins. Nora spends most of her free time playing softball, soccer, and tennis. Cora spends most of her free time reading, painting, and drawing. Both Nora and Cora take piano lessons. But Nora and Cora have different feelings about playing the piano. Cora is bored by her piano lessons.

1. _____Nora and Cora both love sports.

2. _____Cora is more interested in art than Nora is.

3. _____Nora and Cora both take piano lessons.

4. _____Nora and Cora feel the same way about everything.

5. _____Nora and Cora look the same and are the same age.

Willy and Jorge both work as clerks in the same video store. Willy always recommends comedies. Jorge likes to recommend more serious movies. Whenever anyone asks Willy about a movie, he always knows the answer. So does Jorge, but Willy gives his opinions. Jorge is shy about giving opinions, and spends less time talking to the customers. Willy plans to be a movie actor. Jorge wants to be a movie director.

6. _____Willy and Jorge both want to work in the movies.

7. _____Jorge is more talkative than Willy.

8. _____Willy and Jorge work at the same video store.

8 Book 4/Unit 4
Scruffy

At Home: Have students think of a favorite story. Then have them tell how two characters in the story are alike and different.

112

Vocabulary

Write a word from the list to complete each sentence.

| affection | climate | clinging | methods | threat | injury |

1. A cat is a _____ to a mouse's safety.

2. The man was _____ to the life preserver to keep from drowning.

3. Countries near the equator have a warm _____.

4. Lui showed great _____ for his grandfather.

5. Dr. Wilson told Mabel her _____ would heal in three weeks.

6. Although the detective used strange _____, he solved almost every case.

/6

Story Comprehension

Reteach 114

Circle the words that correctly complete each sentence about "Scruffy."

1. In Scruffy's wolf pack, Scruffy plays the role of _____.

   alpha male   alpha female   main baby-sitter

2. The dominant wolves _____.

   beat up Scruffy   fear Scruffy   make Scruffy leave

3. Scruffy teaches the pups to be _____.

   afraid of all wolves   tough   fast

4. In a wolf pack, each adult wolf must _____.

   climb icebergs   baby-sit   fit in and play a role

5. Scruffy got his name because he was _____.

   well-groomed   messy   very thin

McGraw-Hill School Division

Read a Bar Graph

> All graphs are pictures. A **bar graph** is a good way to display and compare pieces of information quickly and easily.

Wolves aren't the only animals that have been endangered. The California condor was at risk, but has made a comeback. Use the bar graph to answer the questions about Condors.

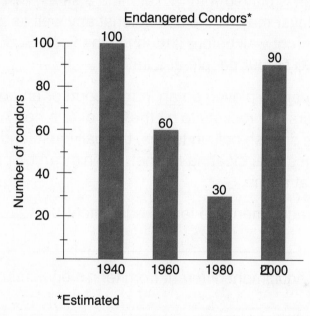

Endangered Condors*

*Estimated

1. In which year was the number of California condors the greatest?

_____

2. In which year was the number of California condors the least?

_____

3. What was the decrease in number of California condors between 1940 and

   1980? _____

4. In which year was the estimated number of California condors about 60?

_____

5. Between 1980 and 2000, how much did the number of California condors

   increase by? _____

5 Book 4/Unit 4
Scruffy

At Home: Have students write and answer one more question about the graph.

115

Compare and Contrast

> When you **compare and contrast**, think about how things are alike and different.

Read the selection. Then answer the questions.

Squash is a sport that is played on an indoor court with four walls. Squash is played with rackets and a small, hard rubber ball. In squash, a player may hit the ball against any wall as long as it reaches the front wall before it touches the floor. Squash can be played by two or four people at a time.

Tennis can be played on an indoor court or an outdoor court. In tennis, players use rackets to hit the ball over a net. A tennis ball is larger than a squash ball. In tennis, the ball must land within boundary lines after clearing the net. Tennis can be played by two or four people at a time.

1. How is squash equipment like tennis equipment? _____

_____

2. How is squash equipment different from tennis equipment? _____

_____

3. How are the places where tennis and squash are played alike? _____

_____

4. How are the places where tennis and squash are played different?

_____

_____

5. In what other ways are squash and tennis alike? _____

_____

At Home: Have students compare and contrast birds and fish.

Book 4/Unit 4
Scruffy 5

116

McGraw-Hill School Division

Draw Conclusions

> Paying attention to the details in a story and thinking logically will help you **draw conclusions** about its characters and events.

Read each paragraph. Then circle the letter beside the answer to each question.

> When Manuel got home each day, the first thing he did was check the mail. He was waiting for a letter that would tell him whether he had gotten into a special summer music camp. Finally, the letter came. Manuel ripped open the letter. Then he jumped up in the air and clapped his hands. Manuel had a big smile on his face.

1. Why did Manuel jump in the air and clap his hands?

   a. He read bad news.

   b. He got a letter telling him that he got into music camp.

   c. The letter had no new information.

2. How did Manuel feel after reading the letter?

   a. confused   **b.** sad   **c.** happy

> Chen-li was about to go to a party. But when she looked in her closet, she saw that her favorite blouse was gone. Her sister Lin-yeh must have borrowed it without asking. When Lin-yeh came home that night Chen-li wouldn't talk to her.

3. Why wouldn't Chen-li talk to Lin-yeh?

   a. Chen-li had a sore throat.

   b. Chen-li was tired.

   c. Chen-li thought that Lin-yeh may have taken Chen-li's blouse without asking.

4. How did Chen-li feel?

   a. angry   **b.** happy   **c.** bored

4 Book 4/Unit 4
Scruffy

At Home: Have students draw one more conclusion about Manuel or Chen-li.

117

Prefixes

A **prefix** is a word part added to the beginning of a word. It gives new meaning to the word. The prefix *dis-* means "opposite of" or "not."

Read each sentence. Add the prefix *dis-* to the underlined word. Then rewrite the sentence with the new word.

1. We all watched the rabbit suddenly <u>appear</u>.

   New Word: _____

   Sentence: _____

2. The children never <u>obey</u> their teacher.

   New Word: _____

   Sentence: _____

3. Shimon looks <u>pleased</u> by the show.

   New Word: _____

   Sentence: _____

4. Olga <u>connected</u> the computer.

   New Word: _____

   Sentence: _____

5. Her mother <u>agreed</u> with her explanation.

   New Word: _____

   Sentence: _____

6. I really <u>like</u> green vegetables.

   New Word: _____

   Sentence: _____

At Home: Have students think of three other words with the prefix *dis-*.

118

Book 4/Unit 4
Scruffy
6

McGraw-Hill School Division

Fact and Nonfact

A **fact** is a statement that can be proven true. A **nonfact** is something that cannot be proved.
For example:
Fact: A dog has four legs.
Nonfact: A dog can fly.

Read each sentence. Then circle the word **fact** or **nonfact** to say if the sentence can be proven true, or if it's something that cannot be proved.

1. Geese lay eggs that are made of gold.

   fact   nonfact

2. A horse can gallop faster than a human being can run.

   fact   nonfact

3. Los Angeles is the largest city in California.

   fact   nonfact

4. A person can cause lightning just by thinking about a storm.

   fact   nonfact

5. When lightning strikes, it can burn or electrocute something.

   fact   nonfact

6. Dogs can talk, but most of them do not want to.

   fact   nonfact

7. When the temperature is below freezing, water turns to ice.

   fact   nonfact

8. If you swallow an apple seed, an apple tree can grow in your stomach.

   fact   nonfact

Book 4/Unit 4
Gluskabe and the Snow Bird
8

At Home: Have students tell where they would look to verify the facts they identified.

119

Vocabulary

Choose the vocabulary word that matches its meaning. Then fill in the crossword puzzle.

confusion	freeze	hilltop	lodge	messenger	praised

Across

3. top of a hill
4. to turn to ice from the cold
5. said good things about
6. person who carries a message

Down

1. the condition of being mixed up
2. house or cabin

Story Comprehension

Write an **X** next to every sentence that tells about "Gluskabe and the Snowbird."

1. Gluskabe is a giant who is disliked by everyone. _____

2. Skunk wanted to do great things like Gluskabe. _____

3. Skunk walked through the deep snow in the giant's footprints. _____

4. Gluskabe convinced Snow Bird to stop the snow. _____

5. Gluskabe was able to completely free Day Eagle. _____

6. Gluskabe punished Skunk in two ways. _____

7. The story gives a reason for snow falling only some of the time. _____

8. The story gives a reason for skunks sleeping during the winter. _____

At Home: Have students create two more true sentences about Gluskabe and the Snowbird.

120–121

Book 4/Unit 4
Gluskabe and the Snow Bird 8

McGraw-Hill School Division

Read a Table

A **table** is a good way to compare pieces of data. When you see a table, read the title and all the labels to help you understand how the information is organized.

Average Monthly Temperatures in Two Cities, January to June

Month	Burlington, Vermont	New Orleans, Louisiana
January	16°*	51°*
February	18°	54°
March	31°	62°
April	44°	69°
May	56°	75°
June	65°	80°

*degrees Fahrenheit

Use the chart to answer the questions.

1. What is the average temperature in Burlington, Vermont, in March? _____

2. What is the average temperature in New Orleans, Louisiana in May? _____

3. How much higher is the average temperature in Burlington in June than in January? _____

4. How much lower is the average temperature in New Orleans in February than in April? _____

5. Which city is warmer during these 6 months? _____

Book 4/Unit 4
Gluskabe and the Snow Bird
5

At Home: Have students create and answer questions using data from the chart.

122

Fact and Nonfact

> You will understand and appreciate a story better if you can successfully distinguish between its **facts** and **nonfacts**.

Read each statement. Put an **X** beside the four statements that are **nonfacts**.

1. Moonlight warms the earth and enables the plants to grow. _____

2. There is a snow bird that causes snow to fall. _____

3. A skunk is a small furry animal with black and white fur. _____

4. Seasons are related to Earth's path around the sun. _____

5. Humans have walked on the moon. _____

6. The same amount of snow falls in each place, each year. _____

7. When the temperature rises above freezing, snow will melt. _____

8. Day and night are caused by the wings of an eagle. _____

Now rewrite the four nonfact sentences above and make them factual sentences.

1. _____

_____

2. _____

_____

3. _____

_____

4. _____

_____

At Home: Have students create their own list of facts and nonfacts.

123

Book 4/Unit 4
Gluskabe and the Snow Bird 12

McGraw-Hill School Division

Compare and Contrast

> When you **compare and contrast**, you should think about how things are alike and different.

Read the selection. Then complete the comparison chart.

Barbara and Norton went to college together and earned their Ph.D. degrees from the same university. Both Barbara and Norton studied science. Barbara was most interested in space exploration. Norton wanted to find ways to make people more healthy and comfortable in old age. Now, Barbara and Norton are professors at different universities. Barbara spends most of her time teaching classes. She also travels around the country, trying to interest people in space exploration. Barbara loves to tell people about what she is doing. Norton spends most of his time in the university laboratory, doing medical research. Norton doesn't speak to very many people about his research.

Barbara and Norton	How are they alike?	How are they different?
Education	1. Went to same college; studied science; earned Ph.D.s	2.
Jobs	3.	4.
Personalities	5.	6.

Book 4/Unit 4
Gluskabe and the Snow Bird
5

At Home: Have students tell about how Gluskabe and Skunk are different.

124

Root Words

A **root** is a word part that is used to form many words. If you know the meaning of a root, you can use what you know to help you figure out unfamiliar words.

Here are some common roots and their meanings.

root	meaning	root	meaning
bio	life	graph	write
phone	sound	logy	study of
scope	see far	tele	far

Find the roots in each word below. Then write the roots and the letter of the definition that matches.

Definitions

a. the study of life

b. a machine that sends sound to faraway places

c. a tool that lets us see things that are far away

d. writing that tells about someone's life

1. biology

Roots: _____ Definition: _____

2. telescope

Roots: _____ Definition: _____

3. biography

Roots: _____ Definition: _____

4. telephone

Roots: _____ Definition: _____

At Home: Have students identify the roots of *phonograph* and tell the word's meaning.

125

Book 4/Unit 4
Gluskabe and the Snow Bird 4

Draw Conclusions

> When you **draw a conclusion** you use clues from what you've read to learn something that is not directly stated in the selection.

Read the story. Then draw conclusions to complete each sentence. Circle the correct letter.

> Lucia shook her empty popcorn box. "I want more popcorn, Anna," she said.
>
> Anna looked away from the big screen. "Can't you wait until later?" she asked.
>
> "No, I can't," said Lucia. "I want it now. Mom said you were supposed to get me what I wanted."
>
> Anna sighed. "All right," she said. She got up from her seat and made her way up the darkened aisle to the snack bar.

1. Lucia and Anna are _____.

   a. friends   **b.** sisters   **c.** classmates

2. Lucia is probably _____.

   a. younger than Anna   **b.** older than Anna   **c.** the same age as Anna

3. The two girls are at _____.

   a. home   **b.** the circus   **c.** a movie theater

4. Anna is _____.

   a. less interested in the movie than Lucia

   b. more interested in the movie than Lucia

   c. more interested in eating than Lucia

Book 4/Unit 4
Meet an Underwater Explorer
4

At Home: Have students identify the clues they used to draw their conclusions.

126

Vocabulary

Write a word from the list to complete each sentence.

| connected | endangered | haul | overcome | poisonous | sponge |

1. There are many animals on the _____ species list.

2. This _____ snake was found in someone's basement.

3. The driver _____ the trailer to his car.

4. The garbage collectors will _____ away the trash.

5. With help, I was able to _____ my fear of high places.

6. Were you surprised to learn that a _____ is an animal?

Story Comprehension

Put an **X** next to every sentence that says something true about the story "Meet an Underwater Explorer."

1. _____ Sylvia Earle is a scientist who studies ocean and marine life.

2. _____ Long, deep dives are not yet possible for explorers like Sylvia.

3. _____ A gym suit allowed Sylvia to walk on top of the ocean water.

4. _____ Sylvia feels we still know very little about the ocean and how it works.

5. _____ Sylvia's friend is developing a one-person submarine for her.

6. _____ The destruction of tiny plants in the ocean will probably affect sea creatures and people.

At Home: Have students use the vocabulary words in sentences.

127–128

Book 4/Unit 4
Meet an Underwater Explorer 6

McGraw-Hill School Division

Read a Time Line

A **time line** gives you a picture of times or events in the past. It also shows you how these events are connected.

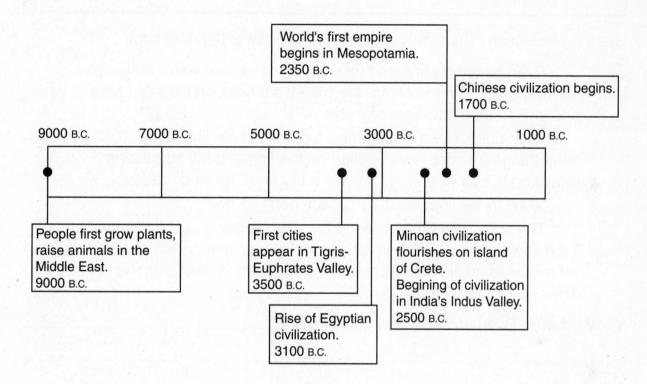

Use the time line to answer the questions.

1. When did the first event on the time line take place? _____

2. When did Egyptian civilization begin? _____

3. How long after the appearance of the first cities did Minoan civilization

    develop? _____

4. Where did the world's first empire appear in 2350 B.C.? _____

5. Which civilization came first, Chinese or Indian? _____

Book 4/Unit 4
Meet an Underwater Explorer
5

At Home: Have students draw a time line to show important events in their own life.

129

Draw Conclusions

> Good readers **draw conclusions** from clues in a story they read. They also use personal experience to help them learn more about a story than what is stated directly by the author.

Read the selection. Then draw conclusions to answer the questions.

Ryan baited his line and tossed it into the blue water of the lake. His friend Tom did the same. Then they sat back on the soft grass and looked up at the clear sky above.

All at once, Ryan felt a strong tug on his line. He sat up. "I've got something!" he cried. Ryan pulled on the line and felt something heavy on the other end. "I think it's a big one!" he said excitedly.

"Reel in the line," said Tom, "and don't let go!"

The line came up and so did the thing at the end of it. When Tom saw it, he couldn't help laughing. Ryan's face turned red, and he removed an old boot from the line. He threw it back into the lake. Then he laughed too.

1. What were Ryan and Tom doing at the lake? _____

_____

2. What did Ryan think he had on his line? _____

_____

3. Why did Tom laugh? _____

_____

4. What kind of relationship do the boys have? How do you know?

_____

_____

5. What would be a good title for this story? _____

_____

At Home: Have students draw one more conclusion from the story.

130

Book 4/Unit 4
Meet an Underwater Explorer

5

McGraw-Hill School Division

Fact and Nonfact

You shouldn't take everything you read as fact. Sometimes writers mix **facts** and **nonfacts** into their writing. You should read carefully to tell what is a fact and what is a nonfact.

Read the selection. Then read the statements that follow. Write **F** if the statement is a fact. Write **NF** if the statement is a nonfact.

Fish are among the most interesting and most varied of animals. While there are many kinds of fish, they all have two things in common. All fish have a backbone and breathe through body parts called gills. They are also cold-blooded animals that cannot change their body temperature. All fish swim in water, and they move easily on land also.

Fish are useful in many ways to humans. However, fish are not considered a food by people anywhere. Many people enjoy fishing as a sport. Some fish, such as certain sharks, can be dangerous and should be avoided.

1. Fish breathe through gills. _____

2. Fish are cold-blooded animals. _____

3. Fish can move easily on land. _____

4. Fishing is a popular sport. _____

5. Fish are not considered a food by people anywhere. _____

6. Certain sharks can be dangerous. _____

Book 4/Unit 4
Meet an Underwater Explorer
6

At Home: Have students rewrite each nonfact above to make it a fact.

131

Root Words

A **root** is a word part that is used to form many words. If you know the meaning of a root, you can use what you know to help you figure out unfamiliar words.

Here are some useful roots to know and their meanings.

root	meaning	root	meaning
geo	earth	ped	foot
mem	remember	uni	one or single
therm	heat	meter	measure
zo	animal	hab	live (in)

Match each word with its definition. Write the letter of the word.

1. _____ making the same sounds or movements at the same time

2. _____ something to measure heat

3. _____ a note to remember to do something

4. _____ a person who travels on foot

5. _____ a device to measure speed

6. _____ something used by the foot to make it run or move

7. _____ a place to live

8. _____ to learn something to remember

a. memorize

b. speedometer

c. unison

d. habitat

e. thermometer

f. pedestrian

g. pedal

h. memo

At Home: Have students check the dictionary definitions for words.

132

Book 4/Unit 4
Meet an Underwater Explorer 8

McGraw-Hill School Division

Steps in a Process

Steps you follow in order are called **steps in a process**. Picturing yourself doing the steps can help you keep them straight.

Read the list of what Tina does when she washes the family car. Then put the list in order from step one to step seven.

Dry off water with clean towel.	**1.**
Rinse car off with hose.	**2.**
Leave car in sun to dry completely.	**3.**
Fill pail with water and soap.	**4.**
Wash dirt off car with water and soap.	**5.**
Shut off the water hose.	**6.**
Turn on the water hose.	**7.**

Write the numbers 1 to 5 in the blanks to show the steps for blowing out birthday candles.

Step _____ Take a deep breath.

Step _____ Remove candles and cut cake.

Step _____ Make a wish.

Step _____ Blow a second time if you need to.

Step _____ Blow out the candles.

McGraw-Hill School Division

12

Book 4/Unit 4
On the Bus With Joanna Cole

At Home: Have students tell the steps in making a paper bag mask.

133

Vocabulary

Choose the vocabulary word that matches its meaning. Then fill in the crossword puzzle with the appropriate words.

abandon	absorb
available	original
research	traditional

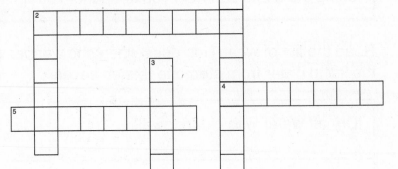

Across

2. able to be used

4. go away from, leave

5. new, different

Down

1. fact finding

2. take in

3. customary

Story Comprehension

Write the answer to each question about "On the Bus With Joanna Cole."
You may refer back to the story for help.

1. Who is Joanna Cole and what does she do? _____

_____

2. Who did Joanna talk to when she was writing *A Snake's Body*?

_____

3. Why is research important to a science writer like Joanna Cole?

_____

4. How does Joanna Cole feel about her success as a writer? _____

_____

At Home: Use some of the vocabulary words to describe a project you have worked on or would like to do.

134–135

Book 4/Unit 4
On the Bus With Joanna Cole 4

Follow Directions

> To learn how to do something, you need to **follow directions**. When you follow directions, you do them in a certain order, step-by-step.

Look at the directions shown in the pictures to find out how to make a snowman. Then answer the questions.

- Freddy makes two large balls of snow, and one small ball of snow for the snowman's head.
- Freddy piles one large ball of snow on top of the other.
- Freddy puts the smallest on top as a head.
- Freddy finds buttons for the eyes and a carrot for the nose.
- Freddy adds sticks for the arms.
- Freddy asks his mom or dad for a hat and a scarf for his snowman's neck.

1. What is the second step in making a snowman?

_____

2. When would you place eyes and a nose on the snowman?

_____

3. When would you show your mom and dad the snowman?

_____

4. If a new picture were added to the directions showing Freddy gathering snow,

where would it go? _____

| 4 | Book 4/Unit 4
On the Bus With Joanna Cole

At Home: Have students draw pictures that show directions for making something.

136

Steps in a Process

> Steps you follow in order are called **steps in a process**. Writing down steps in the correct order will help you remember them.

In "On the Bus With Joanna Cole" you read about how a writer works. You use similar steps when you write a research report. The steps are written below, but they are out of order. Write the numbers 1 to 5 to show the correct order of the steps for the process.

Process: Write a Research Paper

Step _____ Present your report to the class.

Step _____ Research your topic at the library.

Step _____ Write a final version of your report.

Step _____ Write a rough draft of your report.

Step _____ Edit your draft and make all corrections.

Now write down five steps that you would use to write a friendly letter to a friend. Look at the example to remind you of the parts of a friendly letter.

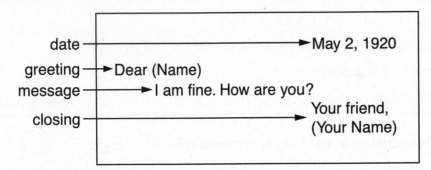

Process: Write a Friendly Letter

Step 1: _____

Step 2: _____

Step 3: _____

Step 4: _____

Step 5: _____

At Home: Have students describe the steps they followed in one of their science class hands-on activities.

Book 4/Unit 4
On the Bus With Joanna Cole

137

10

Fact and Nonfact

> Remember a **fact** is a statement that can be proven true, and a **nonfact** is a statement that can not be proven.

Read the paragraph. Then decide which statements are facts and which are nonfacts. Fill in the chart with five statements altogether.

Buses are a major means of transportation for millions of Americans. Orange-yellow school buses carry students to and from the zoo every weekday. Local buses take workers to their jobs. Intercity buses fly passengers through the air between one city and another. The intercity buses sell mail and packages. Special buses can drive right from the road into water to pick up people who live on islands. Without buses, many Americans couldn't get where they're going.

Facts	Nonfacts
1.	3.
2.	4.
	5.

At Home: Have students find facts in a newspaper article and change each into a funny nonfact.

Prefixes

A **prefix** is a word part at the beginning of a base, or root, word. It adds meaning to the base word. Both the prefixes *dis-* and *in-* can add the meaning "not" or "the opposite of" to base words. The prefix *in-* can also sometimes mean "in" or "within."

Circle the prefix in each word. Then look for the appropriate meaning of the word in the last column. Write the meaning next to the appropriate word.

1. disbelieve		the opposite of formal
2. informal		the opposite of believe
3. dishonor		not to like
4. disfavor		the opposite of secure
5. insecure		money that comes in
6. inexpensive		the opposite of honor
7. income		not expensive
8. dissatisfy		not in favor
9. incurable		the opposite of curable
10. dislike		not to satisfy

At Home: Have students use two or three of the numbered words in oral sentences.

139

Book 4/Unit 4
On the Bus With Joanna Cole 10

McGraw-Hill School Division

Compare and Contrast

Authors often **compare and contrast** ideas, people, and things in their writing. As you read, look for how things are alike and different.

Read the selection. Then compare and contrast to answer the questions.

My cousin lives in California, and I live in Connecticut. We enjoy visiting each other. I like the sunny, sandy beaches in California. We have beaches in Connecticut, but they are not as big. Also, it stays warm in some parts of California all year long, so you can go to the beach any time you want. Back home, it's too cold to go to the beach in the winter.

Both California and Connecticut have a lot of people, but California is a much larger state. It also has more people. Connecticut is an older state and has many more historic homes and places from colonial times than California, though. I guess I enjoy visiting my cousin in California, but I'm still glad to live in Connecticut.

1. What are the two things being compared in this selection? _____

_____

2. How are the two states alike? _____

_____

3. How are the two states different? _____

_____

_____

4. What is one more way the states are alike? Hint: Look at their names.

_____

_____

Book 4/Unit 4
Earth's First Creatures
4

At Home: Have students compare and contrast their state with another state of their choice.

140

Vocabulary

Read each definition clue. Then find the vocabulary word in the row of letters and circle it.

ancestors	disaster	microscope	snout	spike	weird

1. sharp, pointy thing   s t i p s p i k e k e w

2. animal nose   l o z e h i s n o u t t

3. relatives born long before you   c a d a n c e s t o r s

4. strange   w e i r d e a o b s e y

5. terrible event   f e d i s a s t e r o d

6. device for looking at small things you can't see with your eyes   m o m i c r o s c o p e

Story Comprehension

Circle the letter beside the answer that best completes each sentence about "Earth's First Creatures."

1. The ancient relatives of animals as we know them first appeared on Earth during the _____.

  a. Jurassic period   **b.** Cambrian period

2. Scientists call the first appearance of these animals an "explosion" because _____.

  a. their population grew suddenly   **b.** some animals actually blew up

3. The animals that lived just before the Cambrian animals were _____.

  a. almost invisible   **b.** bigger than earlier animal ancestors

4. Some scientists believe the development of animals may have been caused by _____.

  a. the appearance of man   **b.** a major natural disaster on Earth

McGraw-Hill School Division

At Home: Have students describe some of the early animals they read about and saw illustrations of.

141–142

Book 4/Unit 4
Earth's First Creatures

4

Read a Chart

> A **chart** makes information easy to read. Most charts are boxes with labeled rows and columns. Simply read across and down to get the information that you need.

Use the chart about National Monuments to answer the questions.

Name	Location	Features
Capulin Mountain	New Mexico	Extinct Volcano
Death Valley	California	Desert
Fort Matanzas	Florida	Spanish Fort
Glacier Bay	Alaska	Glaciers

1. In what state is Glacier Bay?

_____

2. What national monument is located in New Mexico?

_____

3. What will you see if you visit Death Valley?

_____

4. According to the chart, in what state would you visit a Spanish Fort?

_____

5. Write a title for the chart.

_____

McGraw-Hill School Division

Book 4/Unit 4
Earth's First Creatures
5

At Home: Have students make a chart of places of interest in their home state. Have them include the name, location, and features of the place.

143

Steps in a Process

Steps you follow in order are called **steps in a process**.

Read the paragraph about making hot chocolate. Then write the steps.

> When I've been outside playing in the cold, nothing warms me up like a cup of hot chocolate. My Dad makes it for me as soon as I come in. First, he puts the chocolate mix into a big cup. Then, he puts the kettle on the stove. Just before the water boils, he takes the kettle off the stove. Next, he pours the hot water into the cup. Then he mixes the chocolate and the water well with a spoon. Finally comes the best part. I get to drink the hot chocolate!

Process: Make Hot Chocolate

Step 1: _____

Step 2: _____

Step 3: _____

Step 4: _____

Step 5: _____

Now write down three steps that you would use to brush your teeth. The fourth step is given.

Process: Brush Teeth

Step 1: _____

Step 2: _____

Step 3: _____

Step 4: Rinse toothbrush and put away.

At Home: Have students observe an adult doing something and then write down the steps in the process.

144

Book 4/Unit 4
Earth's First Creatures 8

McGraw-Hill School Division

Prefixes

Knowing the meaning a **prefix** adds to a base word can help you understand unfamiliar words. The prefixes *dis-* and *in-* often have the meanings "not" or "the opposite of."

Underline the prefix in each word in the box. Then think about what each word means. Write the best word to complete each sentence.

dislikes	insincere	dissatisfied	incapable	disqualify
inexact	disbelief	ineffective	disapproves	incorrect

1. The coach will _____ any player with poor grades.

2. If you take an _____ measurement, the curtains will not fit.

3. Mom _____ of leaving me home alone.

4. The child was _____ of reaching the high shelf.

5. Do not say you are sorry if you are _____.

6. The medicine was _____ and the patient got worse.

7. Maura really _____ the smell of cheese.

8. The _____ customers complained to the clerk.

9. Our response to the disaster was shock and _____.

10. Dwain got only one _____ answer on the test.

Book 4/Unit 4
Earth's First Creatures
20

At Home: Have students use five words from the box in sentences.

145

Root Words

Many English words have **roots** that come from other languages. Knowing the meaning of different roots can help you learn many new words.

Here are some frequently used roots.

root	meaning	root	meaning
hydr	water	spec	look
cycl	circular, wheel	dem	people
sphere	ball, round	vid	see
multi	many		

Write the letter to match the meaning to the word.

1. _____ spectacle

2. _____ video

3. _____ multilevel

4. _____ cyclone

5. _____ hydrant

6. _____ democracy

7. _____ inspect

8. _____ spherical

9. _____ multicultural

10. _____ bicycle

a. a place to get water

b. government by the people

c. to look at closely

d. something seen or witnessed

e. of many cultures

f. a circular wind

g. round like a ball

h. having two wheels

i. program that can been seen or watched

j. having many levels

At Home: Have students look for words with the roots listed on the page as they read.

146

Book 4/Unit 4
Earth's First Creatures

10

McGraw-Hill School Division

Unit 4 Vocabulary Review

A. Finish the sentences with words from the list.

| threat | messenger | sponge | available | microscope |

1. The _____ delivered the letter to the office.

2. The musician is _____ for parties and special events.

3. I saw the _____ of a storm in the dark clouds.

4. The scientist saw millions of germs through his _____ .

5. Is a _____ really a sea creature?

B. Unscramble the letters to make a word from the list. Use the clues to help you.

| methods | praised | haul | snout | original |

1. an animal's nose   tonus   _____

2. expressed approval   drapesi   _____

3. fresh, new   igolarin   _____

4. carry   luha   _____

5. ways of doing something   hemdots   _____

Unit 4 Vocabulary Review

A. Read each question. Choose the best vocabulary word from the list to answer the question. Write your answer on the line.

clinging	**confusion**	**affection**	**weird**	**poisonous**

1. If you really liked your dog, what would you feel for him? _____

2. What might you call a dog wearing purple and green hats? _____

3. If you were bitten by a snake you would want to make sure it wasn't what? _____

4. If you couldn't find your homework before leaving for school, what state might you be in? _____

5. If you saw a vine wrapped around a tree in your yard, how might you describe it? _____

B. Supply the correct word from the list.

lodge	**injury**	**freeze**	**hilltop**	**disaster**

We went skiing last weekend and spent Friday and Saturday

nights at a ski _____. I skied down from a high

_____. It was so cold coming down the hill, that I

thought I would _____. We all had fun. The best part

was that no one had a _____ on the slopes or went

home with an _____ to any limbs.

At Home: Have students use some of the words to make a word unscrambling game of their own.

148

Book 4/Unit 4
Unit 4 Vocabulary Review

10

Sequence of Events

In a story, events are organized by **sequence**, or order in which the events occur. Recognizing the **sequence of events** can help you better understand what happens in a story.

Each group of sentences below tells part of a story. The sentences are out of order. For each group, write the numbers 1 to 4 to show the correct sequence of events.

1. _____ Later that morning, Sarah packed her lunch in the kitchen.

   _____ At lunchtime, Sarah ate her lunch outside her office.

   _____ Sarah woke up at 7:00 in the morning.

   _____ An hour later, Sarah had dressed and was out the door.

2. _____ Finally, Jennifer removed the baked bread and let it cool.

   _____ Then she poured the batter into the loaf pan.

   _____ First, Jennifer mixed the wet and dry ingredients for the banana bread in a bowl.

   _____ Then she placed the pan into the oven and baked it at 350 degrees for 60 minutes.

3. _____ The farmer decided to make a scarecrow.

   _____ The farmer secured the scarecrow in the cornfield.

   _____ He got old clothes and stuffed them with hay.

   _____ He watched as the bird flew away in fear of the scarecrow.

4. _____ Mark opened up the umbrella.

   _____ Dark clouds started to gather.

   _____ Raindrops fell from the clouds.

   _____ Once inside, Mark shook the water from the umbrella.

McGraw-Hill School Division

16 Book 4/Unit 5
The Fox and the Guinea Pig

At Home: Have students recount the order of events to research the topic of endangered species.

149

Vocabulary

Write the letter to match each word in the first column with its definition in the second column.

	Column 1	**Column 2**
1. _____	amazement	**a.** turkey and chicken
2. _____	destroyed	**b.** thrown
3. _____	eldest	**c.** shock
4. _____	fowl	**d.** ruined
5. _____	stake	**e.** oldest in age
6. _____	strewn	**f.** pole

6

Story Comprehension

Write a **X** next to each sentence that tells about something that happened in the story "The Fox and the Guinea Pig." Review the story to help you.

1. _____ The guinea pig was destroying Don Emicho's alfalfa patch.

2. _____ Don Emicho owned a computer factory in California.

3. _____ Don Emicho tied up the guinea pig and planned to eat him the next morning.

4. _____ The guinea pig fooled the fox by telling him that Don Emicho was the sheriff of the town.

5. _____ The fox jumped into the deep hole to escape from the fire that he thought would soon rain down from the sky.

6. _____ The mayor of the town gave the smart guinea pig an award.

At Home: Ask students to retell the main events of "The Fox and the Guinea Pig."

150–151

Book 4/Unit 5
The Fox and the Guinea Pig

6

McGraw-Hill School Division

Read Advertisements

> An **advertisement** tries to get you to do something or to buy something. Good readers think about what the advertisement says—and what it doesn't say—before they make a decision.

Read each advertisement. Write the name of the character—Don Emicho, the guinea pig, or the fox—who could most use the product. Then write one question that the character might ask before he buys the product. Look back at the story if you need help.

> ### Get Your Indoor Alfalfa Patch Now!
>
> Are you fed up with unwanted pests in your outdoor garden? Do they nibble your vegetables when you're not around? Then the Indoor Alfalfa Patch is ideal for you! This indoor growing box uses a special light to produce alfalfa patches in the safety of your own home, away from outside pests.
>
> *Act while supplies last.* **Call 123-4567.**

1. Who needs the product? _____

2. What might he ask? _____

_____

> ### Riddles for Sale
> The Riddle Store sells riddles of all kinds.
> If you want to be clever and funny,
> pick up one of our riddles at 65 Main Street.

3. Who needs the product? _____

4. What might he ask? _____

_____

_____

At Home: Have students find an advertisement that made them want to buy the item. Have them write two questions they would want answered about the product before they would buy it.

Sequence of Events

> **Sequence of events** is the order in which things happen in a story. Recognizing the sequence of events can help you understand the story.

Read each statement below. Then write the numbers 1 to 4 to show the correct order of events. Review "The Fox and the Guinea Pig" for help.

1. Here are some events from "The Fox and the Guinea Pig."

    _____ Don Emicho caught the guinea pig in the trap.

    _____ Don Emicho made a trap to catch the garden intruder.

    _____ The fox came along. The guinea pig tricked him into taking his place.

    _____ Don Emicho was upset that his alfalfa patch was destroyed.

2. Suppose that Don Emicho is planting and sowing his alfalfa patch.

    _____ He cuts the grown alfalfa and uses it to feed his animals.

    _____ Don Emicho plants the seeds in the sunlight.

    _____ Next, using a sprinkler, he waters the seeds.

    _____ Don Emicho buys the seeds.

3. Suppose that Don Emicho is having a dinner party.

    _____ Don Emicho makes a list of guests.

    _____ Don Emicho greets his guests.

    _____ Invitations are sent to ten friends.

    _____ Everyone enjoys many tasty dishes.

4. Suppose that the little guinea pig has decided to move away.

    _____ The guinea pig heads out of town.

    _____ The guinea pig gets advice about good places to live.

    _____ The guinea pig marks his route on a map.

    _____ The guinea pig gets weary from walking and rests.

At Home: Have students recall the sequence of events of a favorite story.

Book 4/Unit 5
The Fox and the Guinea Pig 16

153

McGraw-Hill School Division

Make Inferences

> Sometimes you must read carefully to pick up clues about characters and events. When you use clues and what you know from your own life, you are **making inferences**.

Read the story below. Then answer the questions.

"I will not go in there," screamed five-year-old Ashley one early fall morning as she crumpled to the sidewalk outside the school building. Then the little girl grabbed on to her mother's skirt while the kindergarten teacher tried to direct the child into the building.

"You'll have fun on your first day of kindergarten," Ashley's mother pleaded to her daughter, and she picked up her briefcase.

"We have lots of games you can play," added the teacher. "You can play with blocks, or draw, or dress up."

"I just want to go home," Ashley complained.

1. How does Ashley feel on the first day of school? How do you know? _____
   _____
   _____

2. How does Ashley's mother feel? Explain. _____
   _____

3. Is Ashley's mother going home or is she heading to the office? How do you
   know? _____

4. Is the teacher someone who has had similar experiences with children
   before? How do you know? _____
   _____

McGraw-Hill School Division

4 Book 4/Unit 5
The Fox and the Guinea Pig

At Home: Have students make inferences about what will happen on Ashley's first day of swimming class.

154

Context Clues

> Often you can figure out the meaning of an unfamiliar word by looking at **context clues**. The words and sentences surrounding the unfamiliar word are called context clues.

Read each sentence. Circle the letter beside the meaning of the underlined word. Write the context clues that helped you figure out the meaning.

1. Please <u>latch</u> the gate securely, so the dogs won't get into the garden.

   a. fasten   **b.** clean

   Clues: _____

2. The <u>surface</u> of the pavement was too rocky for rollerblading.

   a. the outer layer   **b.** the inner layer

   Clues: _____

3. Her <u>motive</u> for joining the club was to learn how to go camping.

   a. reason for doing something   **b.** excuse for something

   Clues: _____

4. Jackson will <u>substitute</u> in the game for Jamal who is sick.

   a. take the place of   **b.** assist

   Clues: _____

At Home: Have students read a magazine article and use context clues to figure out the meaning of unfamiliar words.

Book 4/Unit 5
The Fox and the Guinea Pig
4

155

Important and Unimportant Information

> Some information in a selection is **important**. It is the kind of information you would include in a summary of the selection. Other information is **unimportant**. That means it probably would not matter if it were left out of the selection.

Read the story and the list that follows it. Write **I** if the information is important. Write **U** if it is unimportant.

Mr. Jones, a science writer for a national magazine, sat at a desk one October morning. He was working in the public library. He was puzzled at the problem with his portable computer. He had just finished the last sentence of a 2,500-word article on killer bees when the screen suddenly went dark. Mr. Jones glanced at his watch. Worried that his deadline was only one hour away, Mr. Jones made two attempts to get the computer to operate properly again. First, he adjusted the contrast button. However, the screen remained dark. Growing more anxious, he turned off the computer, waited a minute, then restarted. Within seconds, a smile of relief came across Mr. Jones' face.

1. _____ Mr. Jones wrote a 2,500-word article.

2. _____ Mr. Jones had a deadline to meet.

3. _____ Mr. Jones finally got the computer to work again.

4. _____ Mr. Jones' article was about killer bees.

5. _____ This problem took place at the public library.

6. _____ Mr. Jones wrote about science.

Vocabulary

Choose a vocabulary word from the list to complete each sentence.

clippers	errands	instinct	memorizing	relieved	sirens

1. Leslie's mother did _____ by herself for a while.

2. Leslie was _____ when her mother wanted a new dog.

3. An important skill for a blind person is _____ a room's layout.

4. Mom jokingly said she might have to carry hedge _____ to cut the low branches.

5. Ambulances use _____ to signal emergencies.

6. It is _____ that makes dogs chase other dogs.

Reteach 158

Story Comprehension

Write the answer to each question about "Mom's Best Friend."

1. How did Leslie feel about Marit when that dog was alive? _____

_____

2. Why do people have to live for a time at The Seeing Eye? _____

_____

_____

3. How was life at home for Leslie when her mom was at The Seeing Eye?

_____

_____

4. By the end of the story, how does Leslie feel about Ursula? _____

_____

McGraw-Hill School Division

Read a Newspaper

> **Newspapers** are filled with important information about current events. There are school, local, state, and national newspapers. Often, there are several sections in a newspaper on a variety of topics. Most important, newspapers are filled with articles. As you read newspaper articles, look for answers to the questions *Who? What? Where? When? Why?* and *How?*

Read the newspaper sample below. Then answer the questions.

THE DELTA CHRONICLE
20 New Graduates Woof It Up!

by JULES GLASS

ATLANTA, MAY 2—Yesterday, as friends, family, and trainers looked on, The Guide Dog Academy graduated 20 new guide dogs for the blind. Situated on Elm Drive, the academy has been turning out first-rate working dogs for the last decade. Each graduate got a diploma and a small gift. The director of the center gave a short speech and praised the hard work of the canine graduates. At the reception that followed, the German shepherd, Labrador retriever, and golden retriever graduates enjoyed a tasty meal.

1. What is the name of the newspaper? _____

2. What is the headline? _____

3. When was the article written? _____

4. When was the graduation? _____

5. Where was the graduation held? _____

   _____

6. What is the article about? _____

   _____

6 Book 4/Unit 5
Mom's Best Friend

At Home: Have students use the information in the article to answer the questions *Who?, What?, Where?, When?, Why?* and *How?*

159

Important and Unimportant Information

> Some details of a story are **important**. They should be included in a retelling of the story. Other details are **unimportant** and are added to make a story interesting.

Read the stories. Write important and unimportant details from each story to complete the charts.

A. Carol knelt down near the kitchen floor to pet her beagle puppy. When she got up and glanced at the stove, she noticed that the bean soup in the pot had nearly boiled over. Carol lowered the flame. After she set the table, she served the soup in purple bowls to her friends Sarah and Jamal.

Important Information	Unimportant Information
1.	2.
3.	4.
5.	6.

B. It was 3 P.M. on a warm spring day. The marathon was almost over. John, the runner on the left, wore a sleeveless shirt and green shorts. Leslie, the runner on the right, ran wearing a brown shirt and blue shorts. Both runners ran neck and neck and felt confident as they neared the finish line.

Important Information	Unimportant Information
1.	2.
3.	4.

At Home: Have students sort the events of their day into important and unimportant ones.

Book 4/Unit 5
Mom's Best Friend 10

160

McGraw-Hill School Division

Make Inferences

Authors do not always directly state everything in a story. Sometimes you have to **make inferences**, or use clues in the story, and what you know from your own experiences to understand what is happening or how the characters feel.

Read the story. Then answer the questions.

It was raining outside. The puppy, known as Pancake, lifted its paws to the windowsill to get a better look outside. Within minutes, Pancake looked back pleadingly at her owner and whined. Then she raced to the front door of the apartment. Alma made a sour face but got up. After Alma lifted the leash off the hook and attached it to Pancake's collar, Pancake barked and wagged her tail.

"Okay, Pancake. I got the message," said Alma with a smile. She scratched her puppy's head and the two left the apartment.

1. What did Pancake want? How do you know? _____

_____

2. Why did Alma make a sour face? _____

_____

3. Do you think Alma has owned Pancake for a while? How do you know? _____

_____

4. What kind of relationship do Alma and Pancake have? How do you know?

_____

_____

McGraw-Hill School Division

Book 4/Unit 5
Mom's Best Friend
4

At Home: Have students reread a favorite story and make two inferences based on what the main character does or says.

161

Figurative Language

> A metaphor is one kind of **figurative language**. A metaphor is a comparison of two things. One thing is compared to something else. For example, *My sister is a peach*.

Read the sentences. Look at the underlined words that show what is being compared. Circle the letter beside the explanation of what the metaphor means.

1. The <u>puddle</u> was the perfect <u>swimming pool</u> for the pup.

   a. The water in the puddle was good for playing and splashing.

   b. The puddle was as big as a backyard pool.

2. The <u>dog</u> was her <u>shadow</u>.

   a. The dog was a dark color.

   b. The dog followed her everywhere closely.

3. On some walks, the <u>dog</u> was a real <u>clown</u>.

   a. The dog did silly, funny things.

   b. The dog wore a funny nose and hat.

4. The <u>tree branches</u> were long bony <u>fingers</u> reaching into the air.

   a. Someone was reaching out from behind the tree.

   b. The tree branches were sticking out.

5. The dog's <u>death</u> left a big <u>hole</u> in the family.

   a. The dog liked to dig holes for the family.

   b. The family felt an emptiness without the dog.

At Home: Have students write a sentence that contains a metaphor.

162

Book 4/Unit 5
Mom's Best Friend
5

McGraw-Hill School Division

Make Predictions

> When you use what you have read in a story to think about what may happen next, you are **making a prediction**.

Read each paragraph. Circle the letter beside the best prediction.

1. Nicholas was afraid of all dogs. When he passed the Johnson's house, their 120-pound shepherd ran out and barked at Nicholas. What will Nicholas do?

   a. cross the street

   b. stop to play with the dog

2. Charlotte liked her files to be neat. Every evening, she carefully tucked them into the proper folders. One day, her four-year-old niece took out all the folders and threw them across the floor. What did Charlotte do when she saw the mess?

   a. let her niece paint on the papers

   b. gathered the papers and refiled them

3. Milagro wanted his father to buy him a mountain bike for his birthday but his father recently has lost his job. Milagro is good at fixing his friends' computers whenever they don't work properly. What do you think Milagro will do?

   a. Milagro will try to get an after-school computer-repair job to save money for the bike.

   b. Milagro will tell his grandmother that his father will probably be unable to buy him the bike.

4. It was late in the afternoon and a lot of students were still at school playing basketball and soccer. Sarah disliked sports but she had stayed late to finish a chemistry assignment. As she was leaving school, she saw three girls leaving with 12 soccer balls. The next day at school the coach said the soccer balls were missing. What do you think Sarah will do?

   a. Sarah doesn't say anything to the coach because she doesn't like sports anyway.

   b. Sarah will tell the coach she saw the girls take the soccer balls.

McGraw-Hill School Division

4 Book 4/Unit 5
The Rajah's Rice

At Home: Have students predict one thing that will happen in class tomorrow.

163

Vocabulary

Read each word. Then find the vocabulary word with the same meaning in the row of letters and circle it.

1. servants   beattendantsy

2. clumsily   shawkwardlyn

3. rejoicing   rcelebratingpt

4. wisdom   owknowledgevzk

5. let go   streleasedth

6. seasoning   yespiceink

6

Story Comprehension

Write the answer to each question about "The Rajah's Rice." Review the story if you need help.

1. What was Chandra's job? _____

2. Why were the elephants sick? _____

3. Why didn't the medical men help the elephants? _____

_____

4. Do you think Chandra made a wise decision to ask the Rajah for rice rather

than jewels? _____

_____

5. How do you think the villagers felt when they learned that the land they

farmed now belonged to them? _____

_____

At Home: Have students tell a family member the most
important part of the story and explain why it's important.

164–165

Book 4/Unit 5
The Rajah's Rice

5

McGraw-Hill School Division

Follow a Recipe

> In order to follow a **recipe**, read the entire list of ingredients and all the directions carefully before beginning.

Read the recipe. Then answer the questions.

Fresh Fruit Cup

2 bananas, sliced   1 large bunch seedless grapes
1 cantaloupe   2 cups pineapple, cubed
1 honeydew melon   lemon juice

Directions
Scoop the cantaloupe and honeydew melon into balls and place in a large bowl. Add sliced bananas, pineapple cubes, and grapes. Mix. Let chill in the refrigerator for at least 2 hours. Before serving, place in individual bowls. Top with lemon juice. Serves 6. If you add a slice of cheese and a piece of bread, this dish works well as a light lunch.

1. How many ingredients are needed for the recipe? _____

2. Which fruit should be cubed? _____

3. How long should the fruit chill in the refrigerator? _____

4. If you wanted to double the recipe, how many bananas would you need?

_____

5. What foods should you pair with the recipe to make a nice lunch?

_____

Book 4/Unit 5
The Rajah's Rice
5

At Home: Have students write the recipe for a dish they know how to prepare.

166

Make Predictions

> When you think ahead about what may happen next in a story, you are **making a prediction**. Good readers check their predictions as they continue to read to see if they were correct or not and why.

Read the story, then predict what may happen next. Circle the letter next to the prediction you choose.

1. "This laundry is really dirty," said Sam aloud as he looked at his muddy jeans and sweatshirt. "I really need these clothes to wear to the game. They are my good luck outfit."

   a. Sam will miss the game.

   b. Sam will wash his clothes.

2. "The box says to add one cup of soap, but I think I'll add more than that," Sam said to himself. Sam measured two cups and poured the liquid into the washing machine. Sam sat and waited for the clothes to wash.

   a. Bubbles started to overflow from the machine.

   b. The clothes washed as usual.

3. Sam's mom suddenly appeared in the basement. She reminded Sam that he was not supposed to use the washer when no one was home. She pointed to a bucket and mop.

   a. Sam will go straight to his room.

   b. Sam will clean up the soapy mess.

4. Sam found his mom in the living room. She didn't look so angry any more. He walked up to her and kind of smiled.

   a. Sam said he was sorry.

   b. Sam said he needed new clothes.

At Home: Have students explain why they made the predictions they did.

167

Book 4/Unit 5
The Rajah's Rice

4

McGraw-Hill School Division

Make Inferences

> When you read, you often have to go beyond the exact words on the printed page. You must **make inferences** about why characters behave as they do and why events happen.

Read each story. Then answer the questions.

> Daniel sat quietly on the living room couch, his head resting on one cushion, his legs propped up on another. Heaps of finished school assignments were everywhere.
>
> "Daniel, do you want to go out for some dinner?" asked his brother.
>
> "What do you think?" Daniel said as he buried his head even deeper in the pillow.

1. How is Daniel feeling? How do you know? _____

_____

_____

2. Why does Daniel feel as he does? _____

_____

_____

> "Wow!" Berto yelled as he read the letter that had just arrived. "They're going to publish my book! It took me three years to write it, but it was worth it after all!" Berto started dancing around his yard, the letter flapping in his hand.

3. How does Berto feel when he reads the letter? How do you know? _____

_____

4. How would Berto behave if the news had been just the opposite? _____

_____

_____

McGraw-Hill School Division

Book 4/Unit 5
The Rajah's Rice
4

At Home: Have students make inferences about family members' feelings based on observations of their behavior.

168

Context Clues

You can often figure out an unfamiliar word by reading nearby words for **context clues**. Sometimes a word may seem familiar at first, but it may be used in an unexpected way. Notice where the word occurs in the sentence and what part of speech it is.

Read each sentence to figure out the meaning of the underlined word.
Circle the letter beside the correct meaning.

1. The Rajah will <u>dispatch</u> servants to get the rice for him.

   a. send away   **b.** help

2. The elephants were held <u>fast</u> to the gate by ropes.

   a. quickly   **b.** tightly

3. The girl was <u>prudent</u> to take rice, and people admired her.

   a. had good judgment   **b.** selfish

4. The people <u>longed</u> for a day when there would be enough for all to eat.

   a. wished for   **b.** measured a great length

5. Many people become <u>furious</u> when they are tricked by someone.

   a. content   **b.** very angry

At Home: Have students use the underlined words in
sentences of their own.

169

Book 4/Unit 5
The Rajah's Rice   5

McGraw-Hill School Division

Sequence of Events

> In a story, events are organized by **sequence**, or order in which the events occur. Recognizing the **sequence of events** can help you better understand what happens in a story.

Read each selection. Then write the numbers 1 to 3 to show the correct sequence of events.

1. The twins set the table. Earlier they had made a wonderful cake and frosted it. Soon the doorbell rang and the party began.

   _____ Guests arrived.

   _____ The cake was baked and frosted.

   _____ The table was set.

2. Jake saw a small cave. He hiked to the entrance of the cave. Inside he fell asleep. But first he built a small fire.

   _____ Jake fell asleep.

   _____ Jake found a cave.

   _____ Jake built a fire.

3. Deidre created a mask from a paper bag. She cut eye holes. Then she added yarn hair and drew on other parts of the face.

   _____ Deidre put on the mask.

   _____ Deidre decided to create a mask.

   _____ Deidre drew on parts of the face.

4. The ship pulled away from the dock. Two days later, we arrived at the island. Who would have believed that a month ago we were just planning this vacation?

   _____ The vacation was planned.

   _____ We arrived at the island.

   _____ The ship left the dock.

McGraw-Hill School Division

12 Book 4/Unit 5
Yeh-Shen

At Home: Ask students to describe the sequence of events in a baseball game. Have them use time words such as *first, next, then, after.*

170

Vocabulary

Choose a vocabulary word from the list to complete each sentence.

beloved	bid	desire	heaved	marveled	permit

1. Everyone _____ at the beauty of the sunset.

2. We _____ a sad good-bye to our friends who moved away.

3. The law does not _____ smoking in a movie theater.

4. She has the _____ to learn to fly an airplane.

5. The sailor _____ the anchor onto the dock.

6. Our cat is a _____ member of our family.

Story Comprehension

Write the answer to each question about "Yeh-Shen." Review the story if you need help.

1. How did Yeh-Shen's stepmother feel about Yeh-Shen? _____

_____

2. Why was the fish so important to Yeh-Shen when it was alive? _____

_____

3. How might Yeh-Shen's life have been different if her mother had lived?

_____

_____

4. In what way did the spirit of the fish's bones repay Yeh-Shen for her love?

_____

_____

At Home: Have students use five vocabulary words in a story.

171–172

Book 4/Unit 5
Yeh-Shen `4`

Read E-mail

E-mail, or electronic mail, lets you send messages by computer. By clicking on small pictures called icons, you can read E-mail, answer it, and even print out a copy of it.

Use the E-mail message below to answer the questions.

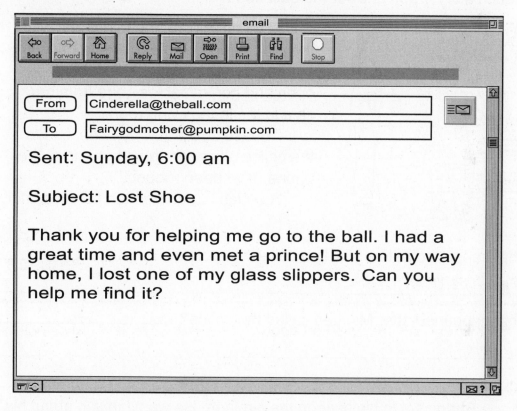

1. Who sent the E-mail message? _____

2. What is the subject?_____

3. When was the message sent?_____

4. Who received the message?_____

5. What icon would you click on if you wanted to send a reply? _____

_____

Book 4/Unit 5
Yeh-Shen
5

At Home: Have students write a reply to Cinderella's message.

173

Sequence of Events

In a story, events are organized by **sequence**, or order in which the events occur. Recognizing the **sequence of events** can help you better understand what happens in a story.

Read each story. Then answer the questions.

Ms. Lee was on the telephone with the police. Moments earlier she had entered her apartment, found the door open and her valuables gone from her safe in the in the living room.

"Please come quickly," she said to the police officer on the other end of the phone. "I've been robbed."

A squad car arrived ten minutes later.

1. What happened before Ms. Lee called the police? _____

_____

2. What happened after Ms. Lee called the police? _____

_____

Burton sat in his seat on the airplane. He was thinking about his first trip to Bermuda two years earlier. In 1998, he had spent two weeks on the beach of the small island. It was then that he learned how to snorkel. Now he was heading back there again. He couldn't wait for the airplane to land.

3. What happened in the past? _____

_____

4. What is happening in the present? _____

_____

At Home: Have students write the sequence of events of a favorite story.

174

Book 4/Unit 5
Yeh-Shen | 4

McGraw-Hill School Division

Make Predictions

> Look at the titles and headings in a selection to help you **predict** what you will read about.

Read each title. Then use it to predict what the text may be about.

1. "Chillers and Thrillers"

   a. scary stories

   b. nursery rhymes

   c. jump rope jingles

2. "Barnyard Buddies"

   a. zoo animals

   b. farm machines

   c. farm animals

3. "From Toe Shoes to Taps"

   a. different styles of dance

   b. the footwear industry

   c. toe problems

4. "Dollars and Sense"

   a. using money foolishly

   b. using money wisely

   c. printing your own money

5. "City Giants"

   a. tall mountains

   b. folktale characters

   c. skyscrapers and big buildings

5 Book 4/Unit 5
Yeh-Shen

At Home: Ask students to look at the chapter titles and headings in a textbook to predict what they will read about.

175

Figurative Language

> Authors use words to create vivid images. They use **figurative language** to create these mental pictures. *Metaphors*, one kind of figurative language, compare two very different things.

Read each sentence. What two things are being compared?

1. The child's cheeks are roses, bright and pink._____

   _____

2. The shirts drying on the clothesline were wild dancers in the wind. _____

   _____

3. The flames were orange monsters that gobbled up everything in sight.

   _____

4. Her hair, black shining silk, made her skin seem pale. _____

   _____

5. The ship was a tiny speck on the horizon. _____

6. Grandmother's words are pearls of wisdom. _____

Write a sentence with a metaphor that compares the two things named.

7. sun and gold coin _____

   _____

8. book and rocket _____

   _____

At Home: Have students write new sentences using two metaphors they identified in items 1–6.

176

Book 4/Unit 5
Yeh-Shen

8

Important and Unimportant Information

> Some information is more important than other information. If you were to summarize a selection, you would include the most **important information** of what you read. You would leave out the **unimportant information**.

Read the selection. Then put a ✔ beside the information that would be important to include in a summary.

Thinking about needing a good night's rest? Well, you are not alone. Most animals, such as cats, dogs, mice, and rabbits, need to sleep or rest just as humans do.

Some animals sleep for long periods. Some sleep for short periods of time. Cats sleep for a long time. Cats are also great snoozers. They sleep up to 16 hours a day. Cats sleep for many hours because they don't have to worry about enemies while they sleep. Other animals are afraid of them or they can climb where enemies can't reach them. No wonder cats can curl up and relax anytime.

Mice and rabbits don't sleep a long time. They need to be alert to danger all the time. They only take naps. No mouse wants to be caught snoring when a cat comes around.

1. _____ Most animals need to sleep or rest.

2. _____ Cats can curl up and relax anywhere.

3. _____ Some animals sleep for several hours at a time.

4. _____ Animals that only take naps need to be alert to danger all the time

5. _____ Cats are great snoozers.

6. _____ No mouse wants to be caught snoring when a cat comes around.

McGraw-Hill School Division

6 Book 4/Unit 5
Can We Rescue the Reefs?

At Home: Ask students to read a newspaper article and identify the most important information.

177

Vocabulary

Read each word in the first column. Write the letter of the definition from the second column that goes with the word.

Column 1	Column 2
1. _____ coral	**a.** spoil
2. _____ damage	**b.** colonies of coral
3. _____ loosened	**c.** 2,000 pounds
4. _____ percent	**d.** skeletons of marine animals
5. _____ reefs	**e.** a part in relation to the whole
6. _____ ton	**f.** made less tight

Story Comprehension

Write the answer to each question about "Can We Rescue the Reefs?" Review the story to answer the questions.

1. What has already killed about 10 percent of the world's reefs? _____

_____

2. How many different kinds of coral are there? _____

_____

3. What does coral look like? _____

_____

_____

4. How can people on land harm reefs? _____

_____

_____

At Home: Ask students to think of one way they can make people in their area aware of the dangers to coral reefs.

178–179

Book 4/Unit 5
Can We Rescue the Reefs? `4`

McGraw-Hill School Division

Use a Telephone Directory

A **telephone directory** lists names, addresses, and phone numbers. The yellow pages list local businesses with their phone numbers and addresses. Businesses are listed by subject in alphabetical order.

Sporting Goods
Bryan's Bike Shop 320 Weston St. 555-6754
Discount Sports Equipment 132 Soccer Ave. 555-1209
Home Run Fun 79 Baseball St. 555-8788

Sportswear
Cathy Dee Sportswear 1867 Short St. 555-7662
College Sports 13 University Pl. 555-4311
Uniforms and More 26 Team Ave. 555-9528

Use the sample yellow pages to answer the questions.

1. What number would you call to reach College Sports? _____

2. What shop do you know sells bicycles? _____

_____

3. What is the street address for Home Run Fun? _____

_____

4. Which business has the phone number 555-7662?_____

_____

5. What kind of information does the yellow pages contain? _____

_____

Book 4/Unit 5
Can We Rescue the Reefs?
5

At Home: Have students look up the name of a local sporting goods store in the yellow pages.

180

Make Predictions

> Good readers **make predictions**, or think ahead as they read about what may happen next. As they continue to read, they check their predictions to see if they were correct.

Read each story. Then circle the letter beside what you predict will happen next.

1. Keisha enjoys basketball. Many other girls in the neighborhood do, too. Keisha says she is going out. She takes her new basketball with her.

   a. She will try to get a basketball game going with some girls.

   b. She will go shopping with some friends.

2. Lee got a snowcone maker for his birthday. At first, he didn't think it was a very good gift. Then, his stepfather said it could be a real money-maker in the right hands.

   a. Lee will give the snowcone maker away.

   b. Lee will make and sell snowcones in the neighborhood.

3. Marco broke his eyeglass frames. The eyeglass store won't be open until Monday, so he can't get a replacement right away. He looks for some clear tape.

   a. Marco will try to mend the frames for now.

   b. Marco will borrow someone else's glasses.

4. Pilar is afraid of all kinds of germs. She won't shake hands with people, nor will she drink from someone elses water bottle. She hears someone cough nearby.

   a. Pilar will leave the area.

   b. Pilar will see if someone needs help.

At Home: Have students identify the clues in the text or what they used from personal experiences to make their predictions.

181

Book 4/Unit 5
Can We Rescue the Reefs? 4

McGraw-Hill School Division

Figurative Language

Writers use **figurative language** to create pictures in their readers' minds. *Metaphors*, or comparisons between two very different things, are a type of figurative language.

Read each sentence carefully. Write **M** if it contains a metaphor, or comparison of two things.

1. _____ The fish were dazzling in the clear blue water.

2. _____ The swimming children were bobbing corks among the waves.

3. _____ Mostly everyone likes warm tropical weather.

4. _____ Sea breezes were the medicine I needed to soothe my nerves.

5. _____ The underwater plants are a maze that can confuse divers.

6. _____ Colorful shells lined the beach.

7. _____ Mom said we were turtles when it came to leaving the beach.

8. _____ Some sea creatures shimmer as they move.

Look at the underlined words in each sentence. Circle the letter of the metaphor that could replace the words.

9. The sea was a <u>muddy green color</u>.

   a. The sea was pea soup.

   b. The sea was a shiny emerald.

10. The fish were <u>many different colors</u>.

   a. The fish were gold coins.

   b. The fish were a rainbow.

Book 4/Unit 5
Can We Rescue the Reefs?
10

At Home: Have students name the two things that are compared in the metaphors they identified above.

182

Context Clues

| If you don't know a word, you can use the words surrounding it to help you define it. Defining a word this way is using **context clues**. |

Read each sentence carefully. Use context clues to figure out the meaning of the underlined word. Circle the letter beside the correct meaning. Then write the clues you used.

1. Stay in the <u>shallow</u> water, so the waves won't come over your head.

   a. deep   **b.** not deep

   Clues: _____

2. My brother studies the <u>marine</u> life in the waters along the coast of Maine.

   a. relating to the sea   **b.** relating to the land

   Clues: _____

3. Shelled animals like crabs walk, but oysters <u>fix</u> themselves to the sea floor.

   a. float   **b.** fasten tightly

   Clues: _____

4. Our boat floated in the <u>channel</u> as we watched the sunset.

   a. land mass   **b.** body of water

   Clues: _____

5. Jellyfish are <u>primitive</u> creatures, not really having bodies and legs as we know them.

   a. not well developed   **b.** newly-discovered

   Clues: _____

At Home: Have students use some of the words on the page in oral sentences with other context clues.

Book 4/Unit 5
Can We Rescue the Reefs? | 10

183

Unit 5 Vocabulary Review

A. Use vocabulary words from the list to complete the crossword puzzle.

errands	desire	heaved	awkwardly	knowledge	reefs

Across

1. The man wearing the cast walked _____.

4. The truck driver _____ the large package on the truck.

5. She does not _____ to go scuba diving with us.

6. I must do three _____ before going home.

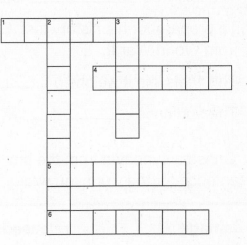

Down

2. Roberta's _____ comes from studying.

3. Colonies of coral form _____.

B. Write the correct vocabulary word from the list.

destroyed	beloved	relieved	sirens

When we heard the fire engine's _____, we were _____. That meant the firefighters were on their way, and our _____ historic building would not be _____ by the flames after all.

Book 4/Unit 5
Unit 5 Vocabulary Review
10

At Home: Have students use four of the vocabulary words in a story.

184

Unit 5 Vocabulary Review

A. Choose the correct vocabulary word for each sentence.

marveled	ton	memorizing	released

1. The fox, was _____ into the wild.

2. To prepare for his history test, Emilio is _____ the important dates from World War II.

3. This feels like it weighs a _____ !

4. The audience _____ at the amazing trick.

B. Chose a synonym from the box of vocabulary words listed below. Then write a sentence for the word you wrote.

damage	released	strewn	eldest

5. loosened _____

_____

_____

6. destruction _____

_____

_____

7. oldest _____

_____

_____

8. scattered _____

_____

_____

At Home: Have students make a crossword puzzle of their own using some of the words on the page.

185

Book 4/Unit 5
Unit 5 Vocabulary Review

8

Cause and Effect

Noticing **cause and effect** relationships in a story can help you understand the story better. A cause is why something happens. An effect is what happens as a result.

Read the paragraph below. Then answer the questions that follow.

One cause of segregation in the South goes back to the years following the Civil War. The Civil War ended slavery in the United States. However, later some southern states wrote laws that denied African American citizens equal rights. Blacks could not go to the same schools, restaurants, or even drinking fountains as whites. African Americans were prevented from voting in elections and running for office.

1. What was one effect of the Civil War? _____

_____

_____

2. What did some southern states do after slavery ended? _____

_____

_____

3. What was one specific effect of the segregation laws? _____

_____

_____

_____

4. Why couldn't African American citizens in the South vote or hold office after

the Civil War? _____

_____

_____

Book 4/Unit 6
Teammates
4

At Home: Have students tell about something that happened in school and then have them identify the cause of the event.

186

Vocabulary

Read each clue. Then find the vocabulary word in the row of letters that best fits the clue and circle it.

circulated	extraordinary	launched
opponents	organizations	teammate

1. very special   l o q e x t r a o r d i n a r y m z c

2. sent off   k l a u n c h e d m d r s w t

3. the other team   z r t y u o p p o n e n t s y

4. someone on your team   u y r t e a m m a t e v c d r

5. groups of people   e g h t o r g a n i z a t i o n s d g

6. passed around   u h c i r c u l a t e d s w v b

/6

Story Comprehension

Write a ✔ next to every sentence that tells something about the story "Teammates."

1. _____ Segregation was legal in the 1940s.

2. _____ Only white players were in the major leagues in the 1940s.

3. _____ Most Americans fought against racial prejudice in the 1940s.

4. _____ Branch Rickey was the general manager of the Brooklyn Dodgers.

5. _____ Jackie Robinson was a star Negro League player.

6. _____ Opposing players treated Robinson like any other player.

7. _____ Jackie Robinson argued with Mr. Rickey about his right to fight back.

8. _____ Pee Wee Reese was a friend to Jackie Robinson.

At Home: Have students use some of the vocabulary words to tell what they know about Jackie Robinson.

187–188

Book 4/Unit 6
Teammates

/8

McGraw-Hill School Division

Use the Card Catalog: Subject Card

When you want to find books in the library about a particular topic, use the **card catalog**. The **subject card** will lead you to books that may be useful when you're researching a general subject like baseball or the Civil War.

Baseball, fiction

JS   Slote, Alfred   **Author**

         Finding Buck McHenry   **Title**

         New York: Harper Collins, 1991 **Publisher**

Number of pages   187   Illustrations

1.   Baseball   2. Negro Leagues

Summary: Eleven-year- old Jason, believing the school custodian to be Buck McHenry, a famous pitcher from the old Negro League, tries to enlist him as coach for his Little League team by revealing his identity to the world.

Use the subject card to answer the questions.

1. What is the subject of the book? _____

2. What is the title? _____

3. Who is the author? _____

4. How many pages does the book have? _____

5. What does the **S** in the call number stand for? _____

_____

6. When is it good to use a subject card? _____

_____

_____

Cause and Effect

As you read, it is important to distinguish between causes and effects. A **cause** is why something happens and an **effect** is what happens as a result.

Read each paragraph below. Then say if each of the following statements is the **cause** or the **effect**.

> Jackie Robinson was a great base runner. Even when he didn't steal a base, he helped the Dodgers win in other ways. Robinson would dance off first base, almost daring the pitcher to try to get him out. Then the pitcher would get mixed up and then make bad pitches to the batter.

1. Jackie Robinson would dance off the base and almost dare the pitcher to try

   to get him out. _____

2. The pitcher would get mixed up and make bad pitches. _____

> Jackie Robinson made the Brooklyn Dodgers a great team. Jackie played for the Dodgers for nine years, from 1947 to 1956. Before 1947, the Dodgers had only played in one World Series in the last 20 years. With Jackie leading the Dodgers, Brooklyn won the National League pennant five times. In 1955, they won the World Series against the New York Yankees.

3. The Dodgers won five pennants and the World Series. _____

4. Jackie Robinson played for the Dodgers for nine years. _____

At Home: During their leisure-time reading, have students look for cause and effect relationships.

190

Book 4/Unit 6
Teammates | 4

McGraw-Hill School Division

Make Judgments and Decisions

Characters in stories **make judgments and decisions**. Readers make
judgments and decisions about what characters decide to do or not do.

Read the paragraph. Then answer the questions.

Jackie Robinson was a proud man who hated to lose. He was
the kind of athlete who never gave up. That's what makes what he
did in his first years with the Dodgers so unusual. Branch Rickey told
Jackie he wanted him to promise he would not fight back. When
people called Robinson, names, threw things at him, or tried to block
him, Rickey wanted Robinson just to walk away. Rickey told
Robinson that walking away would make the other fellow look bad.
To Robinson, walking away felt like backing down. But he knew by
not fighting back he would help the cause of black baseball players.

1. What decision did Jackie have to make? _____

_____

_____

2. Was it fair of Branch Rickey to ask this of Robinson? _____

_____

_____

_____

3. Why was the decision hard to make? _____

_____

_____

4. Did Robinson's decision turn out to be a good one? Why? _____

_____

_____

_____

McGraw-Hill School Division

Book 4/Unit 6
Teammates
4

At Home: Have students discuss a difficult decision they
have made.

191

Context Clues

Remember: **Context clues**, or words and sentences nearby in the text, can help you figure out unfamiliar words.

Read the story, and each of the context clues in the box below the story. Then write the bold-faced word and the letter of the clue that helped you understand the word on the lines provided.

This game had a little of everything. Garcia put down a perfect **bunt**. She ran her hands up the bat and just tapped the ball in front of home plate. Logan, the pitcher, was a **southpaw**. As a left-handed thrower, she had to turn completely around to throw to first base. Logan then made a bad pitch to Zimmerman, and the **slugger** hit it out of the park. The **umpires** would not have to make a decision about that play! Logan recovered and struck out Lee. In the last inning, the final **score** was 5 to 2 in our favor.

a. would not have to make a decision about that play
b. She ran her hands up the bat and just tapped the ball in front of home plate.
c. made a bad pitch to; hit it out of the park
d. As a left-handed thrower
e. 5 to 2 in our favor

1. to tap the ball without swinging _____

2. officials who rule on plays _____

3. someone who is left-handed _____

4. record of runs made in a game _____

5. powerful hitter _____

At Home: Encourage students to use context clues to help them figure out the meaning of unfamiliar words that they find in a magazine or newspaper article.

192

Book 4/Unit 6
Teammates

5

McGraw-Hill School Division

Problem and Solution

Many times a character in a story will have a **problem**. What he or she does to correct the problem is called the **solution**.

Read each of the following stories. Then fill in the charts by identifying the problem and solution in each story.

Olga wanted to have her friend Jin visit after school. But Olga's little sister Jessica was always such a pest. Jessica would play tricks and spy on the older girls. Then Olga had an idea. She asked her mom if Jin's little sister Lei could come to the house, too. Jessica and Lei had a great time, and the older girls were able to talk and visit in peace.

Problem	Solution
1.	2.

Mickey loves baseball, and he is a good hitter. But since he joined the school team, he hasn't made a hit. He knows everyone is watching him when he comes up to bat. Mickey tried extra practice, but that didn't help. Then he asked his brother for advice. Tim told Mickey to picture himself at bat in the backyard, with no one watching. At the next school game, Mickey made a hit.

Problem	Solution
3.	4.

McGraw-Hill School Division

Book 4/Unit 6
The Malachite Palace
4

At Home: Have students reread a familiar story to identify the problem and solution.

193

Vocabulary

Write a word from the list to complete each sentence.

mingled	**feeble**	**scampered**	**cultured**	**fragrance**	**resembled**

1. The girl is _____ because she knows about art, music, and dance.

2. The woman was too _____ to go out in the storm alone.

3. The _____ of the flowers in spring is wonderful.

4. The voices of the children _____ with the music.

5. The children _____ happily across the lawn.

6. The figure on the painting _____ her father.

Story Comprehension

Write the answers to the following questions about "The Malachite Palace."
You may look back at the story.

1. Why wasn't the princess allowed to play with the other children? _____

_____

2. Why did the princess want the little bird caught? _____

_____

3. Why did the little bird stop singing? _____

_____

4. What did the princess make the birdcage into? _____

_____

At Home: Have students write about their favorite part of
"The Malachite Palace."

194–195

Book 4/Unit 6
The Malachite Palace 4

Use the Card Catalog: Author and Title Card

> The **card catalog** in the library helps you find books. If you know the author of a book you want but you can't recall the exact title of the book, use the **author card**. If you know the title, then use the **title card**.

Author Card

Pic M **Call Number**

Author	McLerran, Alice
Title	Roxaboxen
Summary	A spirited group of children use stones, bits of colored glass, and found and makeshift materials to create a fantasy town called, Roxaboxen, which becomes the site of memorable make-believe adventures in the Arizona desert.
Illustrator	Barbara Cooney
Publisher/Date	New York: Puffin Books by Viking Penguin, 1991
Number of Pages	26 pages

Use the card catalog information above to answer the questions.

1. Who wrote this book? _____

2. Which part of the card gives you a general idea of what the book is about?

   _____

3. How would a title card differ from this author card? _____

   _____

   _____

4. Where would you look for this book on the library shelves? _____

   _____

5. If you wanted to write to the publisher of the book, to what city would you

   mail the letter? _____

Book 4/Unit 6
The Malachite Palace
5

At Home: Have students make an author card or a title card for their favorite book.

196

Problem and Solution

Sometimes in a story more than one character has a problem. Read carefully to identify each **problem** and its **solution**.

Read the following story. Then answer each question below.

Brendan's mom was worried. It was the first day she let Brendan walk home from school alone. It was 3:30 P.M., and he was 20 minutes late. Finally she went to look for him. She found him cheerfully talking to some friends. Brendan didn't understand why his mom was so worried. He was afraid she wouldn't let him walk home alone again.

Later, Brendan told his mom that walking home alone was important to him. They agreed that he would wear a watch to keep track of time. He would be home each day by 3:20 P.M.

1. What is Brendan's mother's problem?

   a. She lost her watch in the neighborhood.

   b. She doesn't know why Brendan is late.

2. How does she solve her problem?

   a. She calls the neighbors.

   b. She goes to look for Brendan.

3. What is Brendan's problem?

   a. He wants to be able to talk with friends on the way home.

   b. He doesn't want to walk home alone.

4. What solution do Brendan and his mother agree upon?

   a. Brendan will buy a watch on the way home.

   b. Brendan will wear a watch and get home by 3:20 P.M.

At Home: Have students express their feelings about the two characters' problems and solutions.

197

Book 4/Unit 6
The Malachite Palace 4

McGraw-Hill School Division

Cause and Effect

> Many readers look for **cause and effect** relationships as they read. They ask themselves "what is happening?" and "why?"

Read each story below. Then write the missing cause or effect on the lines provided.

Every year in April we see many snow geese flying overhead. They head north because it is their migration time. This year the cornstalks had just been cut in a nearby field and corn seed was scattered on the ground. This made the field an ideal place for the geese to stop to eat and rest.

1. **Cause:** It is migration time for snow geese.

   Effect: _____

2. **Cause**: Cornstalks had just been cut in a nearby field and corn seed was scattered on the ground.

   Effect: _____

Rachel is upset. Rachel wants to play soccer, but her mom wants her to play the piano. Rachel likes to wear jeans, but her mom keeps buying her dresses. Rachel talks to her mom. She tells her mom she will play the piano and be on the soccer team. Her mom agrees.

3. **Cause:** _____

   Effect: Rachel is upset.

4. **Cause:** _____

   Effect: Rachel's mother agrees to let her play soccer.

McGraw-Hill School Division

4

Book 4/Unit 6
The Malachite Palace

At Home: Have students write what causes a difficult day for them at school, and then what causes a good day for them at school.

198

Synonyms and Antonyms

Synonyms are words that have the almost the same meaning.

Write the letter of the proper synonym for each numbered word on the line provided.

_____ **1.** permitted   **a.** small

_____ **2.** tiny   **b.** labor

_____ **3.** rare   **c.** placed

_____ **4.** came   **d.** watched

_____ **5.** sounds   **e.** allowed

_____ **6.** work   **f.** noises

_____ **7.** positioned   **g.** arrived

_____ **8.** observed   **h.** unusual

An **antonym** is a word that has the opposite meaning.

Write the letter of the proper antonym for each numbered word on the line provided.

_____ **1.** nothing   **a.** closed

_____ **2.** captured   **b.** polite

_____ **3.** friend   **c.** slowly

_____ **4.** rude   **d.** enemy

_____ **5.** heavy   **e.** everything

_____ **6.** quickly   **f.** under

_____ **7.** opened   **g.** light

_____ **8.** over   **h.** released

McGraw-Hill School Division

At Home: Have students write a sentence using two synonyms and a sentence using two antonyms.

Book 4/Unit 6
The Malachite Palace 16

199

Make Judgments and Decisions

> As you read, put yourself in the position of the main character. Look at the choices that face him or her. Think about the **judgments and decisions** you would make if you were the character in the story.

Read the story below, and write your responses on the lines provided. Then help Lamont by finishing his list of reasons to choose whether he should play in the game or go to the workshop.

Lamont is on the school basketball team. He's a good player, but not the team star. The team has worked hard all season and has just won a game. Now the team has a shot at winning the next big game.

Lamont's teacher chose him to represent the school at a leadership workshop. It is a great honor. His parents would be so proud. But, Lamont would have to miss the next basketball game. He knows his team is counting on everyone playing and playing well. Lamont would hate to disappoint his friends and his coach.

1. What decision does Lamont have to make? _____

_____

Take Part in Game	Go to Workshop
I want to be part of a winning team.	**2.**
I don't want to let down friends and coach.	I am only a good player, not the team star.
	3.

4. What do you think Lamont will decide? Why? _____

_____

_____

Book 4/Unit 6
The Toothpaste Millionaire
4

At Home: Encourage students to make a list similar to Lamont's for an important decision they have to make.

200

Vocabulary

| commercials   expensive   successful   gallon   brilliant   ingredient |

Write the correct word from the box next to its meaning.

1. four quarts _____

2. advertisements _____

3. something added to a mixture _____

4. very intelligent _____

5. costly; having a high price _____

6. having achieved something _____

Story Comprehension

Write a ✔ next to every sentence that tells something about "The Toothpaste Millionaire."

_____ **1.** Rufus saw that toothpaste in the store was inexpensive.

_____ **2.** Baking soda was the main ingredient in Rufus's toothpaste.

_____ **3.** Rufus made a one-cent profit on each jar of his toothpaste.

_____ **4.** Rufus called his new toothpaste "Sparkle and Shine."

_____ **5.** Rufus paid all his friends to work for him.

_____ **6.** Rufus gave his friends stock in the toothpaste company.

_____ **7.** It was decided that tubes made better containers than jars.

_____ **8.** The bank gave Rufus a loan to get the tube-filling machine he needed.

_____ **9.** The kids made a commercial to sell more toothpaste.

_____ **10.** The toothpaste sold out and Rufus closed his company.

McGraw-Hill School Division

At Home: Have students discuss two decisions Rufus made in running his business.

201–202

Book 4/Unit 6
The Toothpaste Millionaire | 10 |

Use an Online Library Catalog

> Most libraries have their **catalog** on a computer. You can search the catalog by subject, title, or author. If you wanted to find information on starting your own business, you might search for the subject "business."

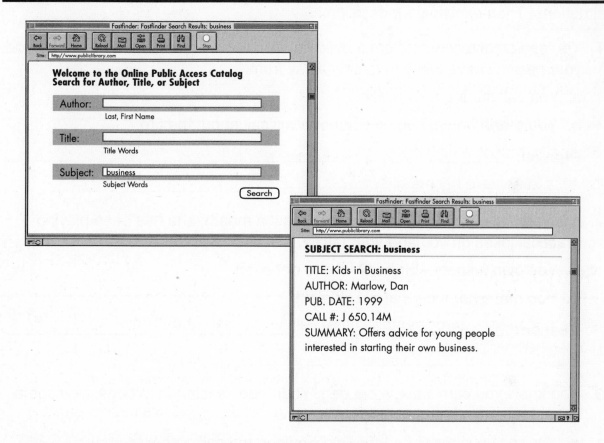

Study the screens above to answer these questions.

1. What is the subject of the search? _____

2. What is the title of the book found? _____

3. Who is the author of the book? _____

4. What is the call number of the book? _____

5. What is the book about? _____

_____

5

Book 4/Unit 6
The Toothpaste Millionaire

At Home: Have students do a subject search on an online catalog.

Make Judgments and Decisions

> Characters make **judgments and decisions**. You do, too, every day.

Circle the letter beside what you would do in each of the following situations. Then explain your decision.

1. You see smoke coming from a building. You are in a part of the neighborhood your parents have told you to stay away from.

   a. You call the fire department.

   b. You return home, hoping someone will call about the fire.

   Reason: _____

   _____

2. It is your little sister's birthday. For at least a month, she has been playing practical jokes on you and your family.

   a. You plan a special birthday joke to get even.

   b. You make her a card and a little gift.

   Reason: _____

   _____

3. You know you can't have a pet dog. Your mom is allergic to dogs. You see a cute stray on your street.

   a. You put up signs to find the dog's owner and call a shelter.

   b. You think the dog is small enough to hide and take it home.

   Reason: _____

   _____

4. You find an empty wallet, except for a name and address card. It is the kind you always wanted.

   a. You keep the wallet, since it is empty anyway.

   b. You call the owner and return it.

   Reason: _____

   _____

At Home: Have students explain the reasons for deciding what they did in a situation.

204

Book 4/Unit 6
The Toothpaste Millionaire 8

McGraw-Hill School Division

Problem and Solution

Noting characters' **problems and the solutions** they find will help you better understand a story.

Read the story below. Then write your responses on the lines provided.

The sixth-grade class wanted to see live whales in the ocean. Nate called for information about a whale-watching trip. It cost $35 per person. For 20 students, one teacher, and four parents, the cost would be $875. The PTA offered to pay $300. The students said they could each afford $10. That left $375 to be raised.

The students decided to hold a car wash and bake sale. A nice day brought a long line of cars. While waiting for their cars, customers bought the delicious baked goods. At the end of the day, the students had raised all the money they needed for the trip.

1. What is the students' problem? _____

2. Rate the problem on a scale of 1 to 4. A 4 means it is hard to solve. Explain
   your rating. _____

   _____

3. In what two ways do the students solve the problem? _____

   _____

4. Rate the solution on a scale of 1 to 4. A 4 means it was a great solution.

   Explain your answer. _____

   _____

McGraw-Hill School Division

 Book 4/Unit 6
The Toothpaste Millionaire

At Home: Have students explain how they would solve the problem of needing money to buy something important to them.

205

Synonyms and Antonyms

> **Synonyms** are words that have the same meaning. **Antonyms** are words with opposite meanings.

Read the words below. Then circle the word *synonym* or *antonym* depending on whether the pair of words are similar or opposites.

1. exactly/precisely   Synonym   Antonym
2. forgot/remembered   Synonym   Antonym
3. borrow/lend   Synonym   Antonym
4. profits/losses   Synonym   Antonym
5. silly/foolish   Synonym   Antonym
6. customer/buyer   Synonym   Antonym
7. walk/stroll   Synonym   Antonym
8. bring/take   Synonym   Antonym
9. expensive/cheap   Synonym   Antonym
10. friends/pals   Synonym   Antonym
11. beautiful/pretty   Synonym   Antonym
12. sold/bought   Synonym   Antonym

Write a synonym or antonym for each word, as directed. If you need to, use a dictionary or thesaurus for help.

1. Antonym   ugly   _____
2. Synonym   talk   _____
3. Synonym   demonstrate   _____
4. Antonym   fancy   _____
5. Antonym   filled   _____
6. Synonym   drama   _____

At Home: Have students write lists of synonym and antonym pairs they would like to use in their personal writing.

206

Book 4/Unit 6
The Toothpaste Millionaire
18

Compare and Contrast

> Writers often **compare and contrast** two or more things in a story or an article to show how things are alike and different.

Read the selection below. Then decide if each numbered statement tells about all the big cats, lions, or leopards. Circle the letter of your answer.

Big cats have many things in common. They all are built for hunting and killing. They have sharp pointed teeth and razor-sharp claws. They also have keen senses.

Lions are the most recognizable of the big cats. The males have distinctive manes. Most lions are a beautiful tawny color. Unlike other cats, lions are social animals. They live in groups called prides.

Leopards are much smaller than lions. They have a yellowish coat with black spots. Unlike other cats, leopards are skillful climbers who lay in wait high in tree branches.

1. They have keen senses.

   a. lions   **b.** leopards   **c.** all big cats

2. The males have distinctive manes.

   a. lions   **b.** leopards   **c.** all big cats

3. They are skillful climbers.

   a. lions   **b.** leopards   **c.** all big cats

4. They are built for hunting and killing.

   a. lions   **b.** leopards   **c.** all big cats

5. They live in groups called prides.

   a. lions   **b.** leopards   **c.** all big cats

5   Book 4/Unit 6
Whales

At Home: Have students draw a diagram to show the similarities and differences between two animals.

207

Vocabulary

Unscramble each word by using the clues for help. Then write the unscrambled word on the line provided.

identify	mammals	marine	pods	preserve	related

1. MALMASM   warm blooded animals   _____

2. SDOP   whale herd   _____

3. ENIRAM   relating to the oceans   _____

4. DLEATRE   connected to in some way   _____

5. YFITNEDI   to name   _____

6. ERESRPVE   save   _____

Story Comprehension

Circle the letter of the words that complete each statement about the story "Whales."

1. Whales are

   a. fish.   **b.** mammals.

2. Baleen whales have

   a. no teeth.   **b.** teeth.

3. The blue whale is bigger than the biggest

   a. dinosaur.   **b.** woolly mammoth.

4. Baleen, or toothless, whales eat.

   a. giant squid.   **b.** tiny fish.

5. There are not many gray whales because of.

   a. over hunting.   **b.** air pollution.

6. The goal of the International Whaling Commission is to.

   a. limit the hunting of whales.   **b.** tag whales for identification.

At Home: Have students recall what they have learned about whales.

208–209

Book 4/Unit 6
Whales

McGraw-Hill School Division

Use an Encyclopedia Index

Just like any other index at the back of a book, an **encyclopedia index** can help you locate information quickly. The encyclopedia index is usually the last volume in the set. The first numbers tells the volume. The second number gives the page the article is on or begins.

Elephant	**6:148** *with picture*
Animal	**1:345** *with picture*; (table) **1:354**
African Animals	**1:246**
Conservation	**4:374**
Endangered Species	**5:201** (table)
India	**10:346** *with picture*
Zoos	**21:232** *with picture*

Use the sample index entry above to answer the questions.

1. What is the main entry? _____

2. In which volume would you find a picture of an Indian elephant? _____

3. On what page would you begin reading about African animals? _____

4. In what volume and on what page would you find information about

   endangered species? _____

5. Why would you use an encyclopedia index? _____

_____

_____

_____

_____

5 Book 4/Unit 6
Whales

At Home: Have students use a home or school encyclopedia index to find references pertaining to dolphins.

210

Compare and Contrast

Jotting down likenesses and differences in a chart can make **comparing and contrasting** two or more things easier.

Read the chart below, and then answer the questions.

Crocodiles	Whales
reptiles/cold-blooded	mammals/warm-blooded
good swimmers	good swimmers
air-breathers	air-breathers
swim mostly in fresh water	swim in salty ocean water
can move on land	cannot move on land
lay eggs that will hatch on land	bear live young in water

1. What are two things crocodiles and whales have in common? _____

_____

2. What is different about where the animals swim? _____

_____

3. Which animals cannot move on land? _____

4. What is different about where the animals give birth? _____

_____

5. If the crocodile is cold-blooded, which means its body temperature changes according to the temperature of the surrounding air or water, what do you

think the body temperature of the mammal does? _____

_____

At Home: Have students compare and contrast two kinds of trees.

211

Book 4/Unit 6
Whales 5

McGraw-Hill School Division

Make Judgments and Decisions

> As you read, try to use what you know to be right and wrong, wise and unwise from your own experience to help you understand a character's **judgments and decisions**.

Read the following story and then answer the questions.

The royal princess complained to the king. She had requested that the royal carpenter adjust her throne. She had asked that the silver at the top be changed to gold and that the gold at the bottom be changed to silver. The legs of the throne needed to be made shorter, and the arm rests had to be padded with blue velvet. Now her throne was ruined. The carpenter had made the whole throne red velvet and the legs twice as long. She insisted that the old, hard-of-hearing carpenter did everything wrong on purpose. She wanted him put in jail.

The king asked if she had made a list of her requests, so the carpenter would have a record of what to do. "No," she said. "It is not the work of a princess to make lists!"

1. What must the king decide? _____

_____

2. Why do you think the king asked if the princess had given the carpenter a list?

_____

_____

3. How do you think the king responded to the princess's statement that lists were not her work? _____

_____

4. In whose favor will the king decide? _____

_____

_____

Book 4/Unit 6
Whales
4

At Home: Have students explain why they think the king favored who they said he did.

212

Context Clues

> Remember: **Context clues**, or nearby words, phrases, and sentences can help you to figure out unfamiliar words.

Read the paragraph. Then read each context clue below and write the boldface word it helps to explain on the line provided.

> One kind of dolphin is the **bottlenose dolphin**. It looks like what it is named for. They are amazing animals. A dolphin mother trains her baby, or **calf**, by "talking" to it so it will recognize her sounds. Dolphins use **echolocation** to communicate with each other and to find their way around the ocean. That means they send out a series of squeaks and sounds and then listen for the echo back to figure out where things are. Dolphins eat a lot of fish, **squid**, and other sea animals. Dolphins use **fluking**, or slapping of the tail, to move themselves forward.

1. slapping of the tail

_____

2. series of squeaks and sounds; listen for the echo back

_____

3. and other sea animals

_____

4. looks like what it is named for

_____

5. her baby

_____

At Home: Have students share the information they have learned about dolphins.

213

Book 4/Unit 6
Whales 5

Cause and Effect

The **cause** is why something happens and what happens is the **effect**.

Read the paragraph below. Then write sentences to answer the questions about causes and effects on the lines provided.

People don't intend to harm our planet, but they cause environmental problems because they don't think about the effects of their actions. A good example is flood prevention on the Mississippi River. For centuries, the great river has overflowed its banks. Billions of dollars have been spent on projects to keep the river from flooding. The river still floods, though. Some experts argue that the flood prevention projects have only made the floods worse. Additionally, wetlands have been filled in. The consequences of this loss of habitat are serious changes in animal and plant life.

1. What is the general cause of environmental problems? _____

_____

_____

2. What has been the general and disappointing effect of efforts to stop the

Mississippi from flooding? _____

_____

3. What cause of flooding do experts argue about? _____

_____

_____

4. What are two other effects of the flood prevention program? _____

_____

_____

Book 4/Unit 6
Saving the Everglades
4

At Home: Have students identify some effects of air and water pollution.

214

Vocabulary

Write the letter of the word that matches the numbered definitions on the lines provided.

_____ **1.** to wait in hiding   **a.** soggy

_____ **2.** is similar to   **b.** importance

_____ **3.** an example or case   **c.** compares

_____ **4.** very wet   **d.** lurk

_____ **5.** animals in nature   **e.** wildlife

_____ **6.** significance   **f.** instance

◿ 6

Story Comprehension

Write the letter of the word or words that complete each statement about "Saving the Everglades."

1. The Everglades are in the state of _____.

  a. New York   **b.** Florida

2. Builders tried to _____ the swamp to get usable land.

  a. drain   **b.** cover over

3. _____ build canals and dikes to stop flooding.

  a. Home owners   **b.** Engineers

4. Fertilizers and other chemicals changed _____ in the Everglades.

  a. water temperature   **b.** plant life

5. Most people feel strongly that it is _____ to save the Everglades.

  a. possible   **b.** impossible

McGraw-Hill School Division

At Home: Have students draw a picture of a crocodile or alligator.

215–216

Book 4/Unit 6
Saving the Everglades

◿ 5

Use the Internet

The **Internet** is a useful research tool on your computer. With a simple point and click, you can find information on just about anything.

Read the following text from a website home page. Then use the menu on the computer to answer the questions.

If you were interested in information about Yellowstone National Park, a good starting place would be the national park home page. You can find it at http://www.nps.gov/yell/. This home page will direct you to many different topics that you can read by moving your pointer to the topic and clicking. Each topic will lead you to other topics. At the end of the home page there is also a link to other pages or websites.

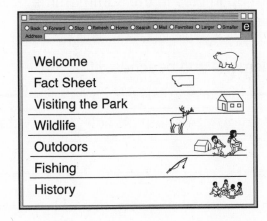

1. What is this website about? _____

2. Which item would you click on to find out about animals living in the park?

   _____

3. Which item would you click on to learn about camping? _____

4. If you wanted a map of the park, which item would help? _____

5. Where would you look for information about the park's past? _____

At Home: Have students list at least three topics they would like to research using the Internet.

Compare and Contrast

Writers often **compare and contrast** two or more things. They point out how the things are alike and different.

Read the paragraphs below. Then write your responses on the lines provided.

Some people call lemons the sunny fruit. The bright yellow color reminds them of the sun. Lemons have a thick skin that protects the juice and pulp inside. The zesty tart flavor of lemons is just perfect in cakes, candies, and drinks. Lemons ship well and are available throughout our country.

Peaches are an orange pink color. They have a soft, fuzzy skin. The flesh of a ripe peach is soft, and the flavor is sweet. People often eat peaches out of their hands. They make a great snack. Peaches often turn up in pies in the summertime. Peaches bruise easily and must be shipped with care.

List four ways in which lemons and peaches differ.

1. _____

_____

2. _____

_____

3. _____

_____

4. _____

_____

5. Although it is not stated, what is one way lemons and peaches are alike?

_____

_____

At Home: Have students compare and contrast themselves with another family member.

218

Book 4/Unit 6
Saving the Everglades
5

Context Clues

> Readers often can figure out unfamiliar words by using **context clues**, or nearby words.

Read the paragraph. Look for context clues to help you figure out the meanings of the words in boldface.

The Rocky Mountains are important for more than their **soaring** height and rugged beauty. In the middle of the **range**, you come to the Continental Divide. The term means just what it says. The top of the mountains divide the continent's rivers. Those running down the western **slope** end up in the Pacific Ocean. Rivers running down the eastern slope end up in the Atlantic Ocean. Between the peaks and the **tree line** you can find beautiful **alpine**, or mountain, meadows covered with flowers in summer.

Context Clues
a. or mountain
b. height; skyward
c. rivers running down
d. between the peaks and ...are meadows
e. Rocky Mountains; middle of the

Write the letter of the context clue and the word it helped you define next to each word's definition.

Definitions

1. rising upward _____

2. slanting surface _____

3. highest point at which trees grow _____

4. chain of mountains _____

5. as in the Alps or Alp Mountain range _____

5 Book 4/Unit 6
Saving the Everglades

At Home: Have students use the words in boldface to tell a story.

219

Synonyms and Antonyms

> **Synonyms** have almost the same meaning. **Antonyms** have opposite meanings.

Choose one of the synonyms below to replace the underlined word in each sentence. Write your answers on the line provided.

correct	vanishing	wet	huge	hurt

1. Swamps are <u>soggy</u> places. _____

2. Fertilizers have <u>harmed</u> the environment. _____

3. The Everglades is a <u>large</u> swamp. _____

4. Swamps need the <u>right</u> amount of water at the right time. _____

5. Some plants and flowers in the Everglades are <u>disappearing</u>. _____

_____

Choose one of the antonyms below to replace the underlined word in each sentence.

awareness	vast	soggy	shrinking	harmed

1. All across the country, wetland areas are <u>growing</u>. _____

2. There is widespread <u>ignorance</u> of the importance of wetlands. _____

_____

3. The Everglades is a <u>tiny</u> swamp. _____

4. Fertilizers have <u>helped</u> the environment. _____

5. Swamps are <u>dry</u> places. _____

At Home: Have students use some of the words above to make a synonym and antonym chart.

220

Book 4/Unit 6
Saving the Everglades /10

McGraw-Hill School Division

Unit 6 Vocabulary Review

A. Use the words from the list below to complete each sentence.

fragrance	preserve	teammate	gallon	launched

1. Pee Wee Reese was Jackie Robinson's _____.

2. Scientists _____ a search for whales all over the world.

3. The flowers had a sweet _____.

4. Please buy a _____ of milk at the store.

5. Many people are working to _____ the environment.

B. Unscramble each word and write it on the line provided. Then write the letter of the correct definition of the word from the list below.

circulated	pods	compares	brilliant	feeble

Definitions
a. whale herds
b. weak
c. is similar to
d. passed around
e. very smart

1. REMCOPAS   _____

2. DOPS   _____

3. NTAILILRB   _____

4. ELEFEB   _____

5. DTEALUCRIC   _____

At Home: Have students use some of the words above to create their own word search game.

Unit 6 Vocabulary Review

A. Choose a word from the list to complete each statement.

mammals	opponents	wildlife	cultured	ingredient

1. People who compete with you in a sport are examples of _____.

2. Opera fans, art historians, and drama critics are examples of people who are considered _____.

3. Bears, dogs, and pigs are all _____.

4. Flour, sugar, milk, and eggs are each an example of an _____.

5. Tigers, giraffes, and zebras are examples of _____.

B. Choose the correct word from the list to complete the sentences below.

commercials	successful	mingled	resembled	organizations

It was an impressive party. _____ people from many different _____ attended. They _____ with each other for a while. Then they watched the new _____ for their organizations on a huge television monitor. Someone remarked that the party itself _____ a television show.

At Home: Write additional sentences for the vocabulary words in exercise A.

222

Book 4/Unit 6
Unit 6 Vocabulary Review

10

McGraw-Hill School Division